And Thus Will I Freely Sing

To Darling Cathrine —
Much Love,
Alexx

Mo chrā cheal thú.
19/9/89

And Thus Will I Freely Sing

AN ANTHOLOGY OF LESBIAN AND GAY WRITING FROM SCOTLAND

edited by Toni Davidson

introduced by Edwin Morgan

Polygon
Edinburgh

First published in 1989 by Polygon, 22 George Square, Edinburgh

Translation of John Henry Mackay used with permission of
Southernwood Press, Amsterdam and © Hubert Kennedy 1988

'Elijah and Isaac' first appeared in *Not Love Alone* (GMP, 1985)

'From A City Balcony' and 'Floating off to Timor' are from Edwin Morgan's *Poems of Thirty Years* published by Carcanet, Manchester, and are used with permission

A version of 'Rab's Story' appeared in *Gay Scotland*

'The Longest Journey' appeared in the first issue of *Man Alive* (1987)

Sandra Marshall's piece was delivered at the Pastoral Approaches to Homosexuality Conference at Pitlochry in 1980 (© SHRG)

Typeset by Hewer Text Composition Services, Edinburgh

Printed in Great Britain by Billing and Sons, Worcester

British Library Cataloguing in Publication Data
And thus will I freely sing.
1. English literature. Scottish writers, 1945–
Anthologies
I. Davidson, Toni
820.8'09411

ISBN 0 7486 6024 0

Set in Linotron 11 on 13pt Sabon

The Nameless Love

John Henry Mackay

Because still on the youthful wing
    The scent of innocent beauty lies
    That touched by a stranger scatters and dies—

This love must I tenderly sing.

Yet since you think it a dirty thing
    Have dragged it through mud and infamy
    And kept in the dark under lock and key—

This love will I freely sing.

To love's persecuted my song I bring
    And to the outcasts of our time
    Since happy or not this love is mine—

This love dare I loudly sing.

Contents

Preface and Acknowledgements

Toni Davidson

This wasn't easy. The need for a book like this is obvious — too often myself and other writers have sent manuscripts down to London in search of publication wondering whether or not they are 'too gay' but also 'too Scottish'. This book is a small attempt to provide an outlet for writers who have so often been frustrated and patronised because they lived north of the south-east of England.

This can only be a start. I apologise to those reading this thinking 'I could have written something for it'. The difficulty in contacting people for such an anthology and the word-of-mouth nature of most of the contacts I made, mean that the book can only have begun to utilise the wealth of writing in Scotland. Perhaps this book can be seen as the first of many more.

There has been a lot of support for this book and I would like to mention some of the people who have helped along the way. Principally this book could not have got to this stage without the encouragement and support of Emma Healey, whose incisiveness and personal contacts were invaluable. Acknowledgement, too, must go to Craig Mercer, whose advice and knowledge of the 'system' helped this idea to become more than a carbuncle in my head. Respect is due also to Edwin Morgan for his introduction and willingness to help despite myriad commitments. And respect is due to Helen, Walter, Graeme Woolaston for the plug, and to Peter K. at Polygon for unbridled enthusiasm and publisher lunches. And respect due to Criz for putting up with endless doubts and anxiety attacks in the bath.

Submission for a second anthology of poetry, fictions, interviews, autobiographies and histories should be sent care of the publisher to arrive between 1st June and 1st November 1990.

Introduction

Edwin Morgan

Toni Davidson is to be congratulated on bringing together the first collection of Scottish lesbian and gay writing, and as a first collection it rightly covers a wide range of material — documentary, prose fiction, and verse. The tone of the contributions varies from the highly assured to the tentative, but a recurring note of painful and sometimes very moving honesty shows just how important such a collection must be as a first move towards greater openness. Particularly at a time when Section 28 allows an as yet undefined but potentially very oppressive threat to hang over the presentation of gay material, it seems all the more necessary to defend the freedom to publish work based on this inescapable part of human experience.

I thought it was specially interesting that the editor has included John Henry Mackay, since it makes the point that much of what we ought to be aware of lies hidden, submerged, undiscussed. Why was Hugh MacDiarmid, for example, such an enthusiast for Mackay, and how much of his work had he read? In his *Contemporary Scottish Studies* (1926) he linked Mackay with Cunninghame Graham and Norman Douglas as instances of exotic Scottish genius which remained Scottish but needed other lands to flourish in. The year after Mackay died, 1934, MacDiarmid published a poem dedicated to him and presumably written in his memory ('First Objectives'), a poem which reiterates Mackay's anger against authority and indoctrination. And even in 1957, in an unpublished essay called 'Joseph Conrad and His Scottish Friends' (I owe this reference to Alan Riach), he again praised Mackay as one of Scotland's 'great writers' who 'wrote only in German and won a worthy place for himself in German literature as a poet and novelist'. This last quotation shows that MacDiarmid was not merely an admirer of Mackay's anarcho-socialist polemical writings, which we might expect, but knew also of his homosexual poetry and fiction. Yet the books on MacDiarmid which have been multiplying in the last few years do not mention Mackay, far less investigate his influence. This is simply one example, from an area where a large recovery operation still waits to be undertaken, much ignorance dispelled, many connections discovered, and not a few reinterpretations made.

'One day a novelist with that [i.e. homosexual] temperament will have the courage to write about himself as he is, not as he would be were he actually Jane or Gladys or Aunt Maria.' So said Compton Mackenzie in 1927, having in mind the sexual disguise adopted by writers like Proust in devising their characters. Interestingly enough, he himself proved that one did not have to be homosexual to write convincing novels of male (*Thin Ice*) and female (*Extraordinary Women*) gay experience. But he could not have done this if he had not had a curiously sympathetic insight into such experience. His belief that 'one day' writers would 'have the courage' to write about their own gay experiencing of life, and the ability to transform experience into art in less muffled ways, was soundly based, though many a struggle and much self-doubt had to be gone through first.

When I grew up in Glasgow in the 1920s and 1930s, the pressure of what was and what was not to be written about — or even openly talked about — was so strong that any gay poetry seemed doomed to cover its traces by switching from a desired 'he' to a neutral 'you'. Yet the wish to record the truthful emotional basis of the poetry, or at least to embed some fairly clear hints within the structure, was equally strong. In an early love-poem written in 1946 I made use of the fact that both names of the man being addressed were also common words, so that by dropping the capitals I could include his name in the poem, as a code that someone would someday crack; I wanted both to conceal, and not to conceal. To anyone of my generation, the inhibitions were enormous, and habits of disguise and secrecy, inculcated at an early age, are hard to break. It has to be remembered, too, that it is not always the most open and frank poems which are the best; think of Housman and Whitman, where lack of frankness is the very power the poem thrives on! Nevertheless, the stage we want to reach is the one where we can make our own individual choice whether to be frank or not. It is encouraging to see that the younger contributors to the present volume find this a hurdle that has already been crossed, or if not, that certainly can be crossed.

Visibility Eighties Rising

Iona McGregor

In the late Eighties the all-too vocal majority has decreed that gay people shall once more be driven underground. Clause 28/29 is the first step in this direction. The main result of 'shielding' young people from the real facts about lesbians and gay men will be to infect them with homophobia; but I believe there is more to the campaign than cashing-in on public ignorance of the difference between homosexuality and pederasty. It is an attempt to make the gay community undermine itself by returning to the furtive guilt-ridden state that preceded the Stonewall riots.

However, I believe that the right-wing backlash will not succeed in its second aim at least. This perhaps foolish optimism is based on the enormous change in attitudes towards gayness over the past forty years. Not those of the straight world: there I think we must reconcile ourselves to permanent mockery, hostility or — at the best — embarrassed toleration. I am referring to our own attitudes. Our strongest weapon is that we are convinced of our right to an open existence. We have become visible to ourselves. Those of us who are old enough to have lived through these changes should be mildly hopeful.

By the age of seven I knew there was something skewed about my view of the world. Exactly what it was, I could not work out. I was a mystified onlooker as my contemporaries tumbled into crushes on authority figures of their own sex, and then later began to squabble over the attentions of young men. What was I missing? How could my friends see any charm in aged hags of thirty who could no longer run and jump, or in those croaky-voiced youths covered with spots?

Until my teens I sought out the company of boys, because like them I scorned games with dolls and other female interests. The head teacher of the primary school I attended in Dunblane told my mother that I refused to stay in the girls' playground at breaktimes and was constantly playing marbles with the boys. Did she want this stopped? My mother returned a cryptic 'No'.

I was allowed to grow up as a thorough tomboy, acquiring imitation guns, lead soldiers, a Meccano set and a lethal knife which inflicted a bone-deep scar on my forefinger. Its broken blade still comes in handy for opening tins of paint.

When I look at photos of myself at this age I am rather puzzled. The face is recognisably mine in shape and features, but the expression is wary and diffident, not at all what one would expect from the active, outdoor child I undoubtedly was. The expression becomes progressively more self-conscious as I go into my teens; and not all of it can be put down to adolescent awkwardness before a camera. A textbook example of identity crisis, perhaps?

I grew up in an army family, the almost all-male pre-war army. Besides some bizarre tropical memories, this imprinted on my mind a rigid division between male and female roles, even more strongly perhaps than if I had experienced a more conventional childhood. Each sex had its fixed behaviour pattern, and never the twain should meet. Women worked until they married, and then their life centred entirely on the home.

My revolt against these stereotypes took the form of passionately wishing that I had been born a boy. I don't remember when this longing began; probably with my first awareness that human beings were divided into two species and that one was more important than the other. I'm also uncertain whether I identified with the male role because I genuinely found its activities more interesting, or vice-versa.

Eventually I was able to start pestering my parents to do something about the mistake in my gender. We were visited by a doctor who years before had lodged with my grandmother in St Andrews as a medical student. I was about nine years old at the time. The doctor had been practising in South Africa, and was by our standards very wealthy. He was amused by my refusal to behave like a little girl, and made a joke about medical operations and transexuality. (This was very daring for the late Thirties.) I seized on this information; for a time I became obsessed by the idea of changing my sex. I knew exactly what anatomical alterations were necessary. The little boys I played with were already indulging in macho stag games, comparing equipment and seeing who could pee the farthest from the tops of trees.

Freud would have labelled my behaviour penis envy. Of course it was nothing of the sort. It was role envy, brought on by the inequalities that lay ahead of me. And I am quite definitely not transexual. My fantasies disappeared with puberty, although I greatly resented the changes it brought to my appearance and physical functions. I still considered the male role more desirable; but even this preference disappeared like snow off a dyke — so to speak — as soon as I encountered the women's liberation movement. There I found the ideas and concepts to explain those anomalies of my childhood. I began with Simone de Beauvoir's *The Second Sex* and have not looked back since. But my change in outlook was not to come about for nearly twenty years.

When I think about the doctor's visit, I am amazed that my parents said nothing to neutralise his remarks to me. Publicly they showed far more concern about the extravagant presents he gave to me and my two younger sisters. They were embarrassed by a generosity they could not reciprocate, and when he returned to Africa scolded me for letting him buy me a bicycle. It cost three pounds; at that time more than half my father's weekly wage.

I can't remember ever being checked or punished for trying to behave like a boy. My parents made no pointed comparisons with my two younger sisters, who played with dolls and miniature cooking scales. In fact, everything odd or unusual about my behaviour met with a wall of silence. Looking back, I see that my parents preferred not to confront the issue. To the end of their lives they would never let me draw them into my personal problems; their blocking-out was so effective that it was impossible to use the words 'lesbian' or 'homosexual' in front of them.

In later life I was able to bring lovers to my parents' home. They were treated politely, but as friends. My mother became very attached to the woman with whom I formed my most important relationship, and kept in touch with her long after the two of us had separated. She never openly acknowledged the relationship; yet when we stayed overnight, the two single beds of the room in which we slept had always been drawn together and made up as one. As we left, my mother would kiss A. goodbye; when it came to my turn, she would sharply avert her face to make sure that my kiss landed only on her cheek.

My parents' generation found it difficult enough to deal

with their own sexuality, let alone their children's; and parents raising a family in wartime Europe had more serious problems to cope with. Perhaps I should have tried harder to find the right words. Nevertheless their — or our — inability to communicate on this crucial matter affected all my dealings with them after early childhood. Our lack of closeness remains a permanent regret.

As a teenager, I was sent off to board at a girls' school to which I had won a scholarship. Until I was old enough to chafe at the restrictions, I thoroughly enjoyed this new environment. I now think it was a great mistake to go there. At a mixed school I would have been forced into defining my homosexuality much sooner. At this institution there were none of the torrid lesbian involvements described in school novels written for adults. Perhaps this was because the pupils consisted mostly of day-girls. However, among the younger boarders 'crushes' or 'pashes', as they were called, were endemic. These were adoring attachments to senior pupils or members of staff. As far as I know, they were purely romantic. I took no part in them. I was too old and, in any case, since the age of eleven I had been attracted to girls of my own age.

As I moved up the school I fell in love with one contemporary after another, but my beloveds were all unresponsive. Boarders of all ages were almost in purdah. Our contact with male company was carefully chaperoned — an arrangement which naturally delighted me — and their term-time seclusion only made the older girls more avid to find boyfriends during the holidays.

We were all aware of sexual behaviour, in theory at least. Most of the teachers were resident, and we used to speculate scandalously on whether X and Y were 'lesbian'; but the meaning I gave to this word was very hazy. I was as ignorant of lesbian sex as I was of what lesbianism might mean in social behaviour. Incredible as it may seem, I made no connection between my own turbulent feelings and what was said to be going on in the staff bedrooms.

In other words, I was still invisible to myself. I knew with absolute certainty that I did not want to marry. The thought of giving up my own name and letting someone else earn my living was insupportable. But that was as far as I had got. In the 1940s it was impossible to define myself as homosexual and my friends as heterosexual. Although I knew the words, they were not available as social labels to describe my own experience. They were still only technical terms to be found in medical dictionaries.

I was in my late teens, utterly inexperienced, and my urges towards these attractive young women who shared my school life were not precisely focused. All the same, it didn't take long to realise that it would be sensible to hide my feelings. As one unsatisfied passion after another dogged me to the verge of adulthood, I became ashamed of my fixation on what I was taught to see as a necessary but temporary phase of adolescence. According to orthodox opinion, I had fallen back from a leap that the other salmon had made with ease. My belief was reinforced by Saturday night readings when the headmistress used to gather the senior boarders in her sitting room. The books she chose included a fair dose of current psychology. This was intended to help us grow up into good wives and mothers.

Ironically, in 1973 I ran into a younger fellow-pupil at a gay conference. She was helping to edit the lesbian magazine *Sappho*.

When I became a student I was once more plunged into

co-educational society. Many aspects of this I enjoyed; but I cannot say my university days were happy. I was bold enough to lure two of my fellow-students into semi-affaires; but neither of these went far enough to teach me about lesbian relationships.

Most of the stress I felt at university came from my own anxieties about myself, rather than outside pressure. I was beginning to wonder if I was frozen at this adolescent stage because I was afraid of normal sexual relations. It is difficult for anyone who grew up after 1960 to realise the level of sexual restraint shown by most people of the pre-war generation in their youth. We weren't ignorant of the facts of life: our parents might never instruct us explicitly, but we discovered what we needed to know from textbooks and peer-group gossip. The vast difference was in attitudes and assumptions. Among the over-twenty-fives I suppose the level of extra- and non-marital sex was pretty much the same as today; but there was no contraceptive pill, and the bench-mark for young women of all classes was to be celibate until marriage. Those who weren't kept very quiet about it.

In those pre-permissive days, a homosexual woman could escape notice merely by refusing to join in the merry-go-round of dating and boyfriends. Lack of interest roused good-humoured contempt, not cries of *lemon*. The ethos was simple: ambitious or over-studious girls would end up on the shelf. This was also the fate of many heterosexual women who wanted to continue working, or never received a proposal of marriage. Right through the Fifties, it was rare to find married women working full time in any of the professions. However, until one was safely past the marrying years, to avoid the usual pattern of dating for the cinema, theatre, or dance-hall and ending the walk home with some mild love-making, brought the penalty of social isolation.

Now officially an adult, for a short time I veered unhappily between dating and not dating. In 1952, in my early twenties, with my massive personal problem still unsolved, I found myself working in Edinburgh. I pushed myself into a full-blown liaison with a heterosexual man. The experiment was disastrously successful. At last I realised that I was not a psychological freak, but one of a category that existed in its own right. Even if I never met another lesbian, I promised myself, I would never repeat my mistake. I broke off the affaire, rather brutally I think now.

After this, I quickly gravitated to the raffish side of Edinburgh life, where my non-conformity would not be so conspicuous. The city's society was then sharply divided into Morningside and Bohemia, two extremes which confronted each other with mutual dislike. One was as self-absorbed as the other, neither concerning itself with the submerged third world to be found in the Grassmarket, which had not yet been trimmed out with its modish adjuncts.

Bohemia . . . The very word, with its naive associations, shows that alternative Edinburgh of the Fifties was very innocent. The only drug commonly consumed was self-admiration. There was a lot of fornication, as Morningside would have called it, but extra-marital relationships were not publicised outside a small circle of friends. Any casual sexual encounters (and I do not believe there were many) were even less talked about. In that environment I had no qualms about displaying my newly-confirmed identity. I knew what I wanted; I had to find other women who wanted the same, and this seemed the most likely hunting-ground. I thought my problem had resolved itself into a simple quest for a partner.

Other more complicated aspects were not to be revealed until much later.

In terms of everyday reality I had set myself an almost impossible task. I did not know what signals to look out for, and this Fifties world of poets, painters and writers was apparently 100 per cent heterosexual. Its public image was totally male-centred. In Rose Street (then a notorious mile of pubs and bawdy-houses), at the Abbotsford and Paddy's Bar female Bohemians stood dutifully beside their man. They would never have dreamed of ordering their own drinks, let alone entering a pub without an escort. Once admitted into these beery stamping-grounds they were expected to be seen and not heard. Morningside ladies called them unkind names but in self-oppression both sets of women were sisters under the skin. I think I was accepted here because my homosexuality was regarded as an affectation. In the Fifties, a *Lesbian* (note the capital letter) was a woman who had not learned to respond to men. They kept on trying. The identity I claimed was taken seriously by no one but myself.

My own section of Bohemia had its home-base in International House, the nearest to a café society that has ever flourished in Edinburgh. The Assembly and Fringe Clubs are not adequate replacements, because they function only during the Festival. The International provided effortless sociability all year round. It occupied the upstairs corner of Castle and Princes Street, now taken over by hamburgers, providing its members with an informal bar and coffee house that stayed open until what was then quite late in the evening. At weekends it also came up with lunches and dancing — the foxtrot and quickstep variety. Sitting at its wrap-around windows one could survey the scene outside, as if on a Paris boulevard, lingering for hours over a cheap coffee. Evenings were spent waiting to see who would drop in. The club membership provided an extended family for the non- or unhappily married. Many now well-known or notorious figures dawdled away part of their youth on these premises. Idi Amin was one. Morningside (which never ventured in) equated this place with the Hell Fire Club. The International was naturally at its liveliest during the Festival. Every summer I looked forward to the influx of lesbians that surely must descend on it. But they never did. Perhaps they were too discreet to declare themselves to a stranger. August was as unproductive for me as the rest of the year. However, I did meet a lot of gay men there, some of them visitors and some who had made their homes in Edinburgh. Despite the illegality of the male homosexual scene during the Fifties, gay men had no difficulty in making contact.

These friends became the mainstay of my social circle. I fell in with their interests and lifestyle, only too thankful to be free of the pressure of sexual attention. I suspect that some of them centred round GHQ — the in-name for a notorious urinal that lay under the Duke of Wellington's statue outside Register House. One young friend who had been first seduced on a psychiatrist's couch blossomed into a honey-pot each Festival. His greatest conquest was a now famous actor who once flew him to Paris for lunch.

This was the era of high camp, so despised by a later generation strengthened by gay pride. A pale reflection of it lingers on in the performances of Quentin Crisp. Its brittle culture had a natural affinity with the theatre. Not serious or political dramas, but show-biz, revue, musicals and the ballet. Its idols were Marlene Dietreich, Bette Davies, Eartha Kitt and lesser bitch goddesses now forgotten. My friends indulged in obsessive chatter about fashion, interior design, bric-a-brac and the goings-on of public personalities, preferably royal. There was endless discussion as to whether so-and-so was *queer*. The word was freely used, because there was no other.

'It's all right, darlings,' said one friend in happy relief after a very public marriage was announced. 'He's one of *us*. He keeps the head waiter at the —— —— in Kensington.'

My gay friends understood lesbian sexuality no better than the heterosexual men, but at least they accepted it in their own way. Sympathising with my loneliness, they would bring me the centrefold of *Playboy*. Depending on the degree of friendship I would either accept and put it at once into a wastepaper basket, or try to explain that this was not quite what I was looking for.

At the time, I was persuaded that I was enjoying myself. Apart from the one great blank, life edited itself as a series of parties and endlessly amusing incidents. Through necessity I thrust aside my real needs and was relentlessly trivial. It was all light years away from consciousness-raising and the politics of feminism. In the Fifties these were as inconceivable as walking on the moon. Now when I look back all those scenes of my youth seem like so many exotic and artificial stage sets. Even ten years later, I could hardly believe that I had been a part of that frivolous lifestyle. Not because by then I had transferred myself from Bohemia to a sober chalkface in England; but because by the end of the Sixties women's sense of their own identity had changed. As a hard-working teacher in Outer London I did not display my label so recklessly; but I had acquired self-confidence. At last I had the real answer to the question that had puzzled me at the age of seven. I had not yet grasped that other people could take a different route to the place I had arrived at, but I had taken possession of my own reality.

I am glad my perspectives have changed so drastically, yet I remain profoundly grateful to those gay men. I admire the way they resisted the straight world's contempt and hatred, even if they did it from inside a ghetto. My friends were buoyant, amusing, and consistently loyal. Without them I might not have survived to a more liberated age.

So where were all the Edinburgh lesbians in the Fifties? I searched Bohemia for five years, and found very few traces. There was a formidable bar-owner in Rose Street, Eton-cropped, with jacket and tie, who was rumoured to live with a niece in inverted commas. The only time we spoke to each other, it was not sisterhood she had on her mind. She wanted to know whether I had entered her premises unescorted. If I had, I must be on the game. As I was with a male friend I was allowed to drink on.

Nowadays I think that my openness must have frightened off any closeted sisters. I also had the wrong guide-books. My identikit was constructed from the poems of Sappho, *The Well of Loneliness*, and textbooks of so-called abnormal psychology which I read in the National Library on a ticket issued to me for the linguistic research connected with my work. There was nothing else. Lesbian literature was still sparse and all of it tainted with guilty despair. Women's history did not exist. There were no role models, let alone a supportive community. My few older women friends, sympathetic but straight, unanimously advised me to pack my bags for London. Despite the existence there of one or two clubs like the Gateways, I doubt if life was much better in London than in Edinburgh thirty years ago, except for the negative advantages of anonymity. Before taking this advice, I did briefly meet three gay women in Edinburgh. I think the circumstances sum up how it was for lesbians in the

Fifties. I was invited to a party. She was cutting sandwiches, and handing them out as they were made. When I reached the top of the queue, Mary, as I shall call her, put down the bread-knife.

'I think we have something in common,' she said.

I smiled. 'Oh, what's that?' A passion for Camembert, perhaps, or Mendelssohn's violin concerto? Mary fixed me with a yearning, solemn gaze.

'I've been to the Hebrides to think it over. I stood on the beach for hours and hours . . .'

And there she had come to the inevitable conclusion, Mary went on in rather too audible tones. She had decided that she was lesbian.

The queue behind me was getting restless, and it seemed prudent to continue this discussion in a less public place. As we moved off to an empty room (leaving the hungry guests to cut their own sandwiches) I asked myself what she wanted. Was it only human contact in the heterosexual wilderness, or something more?

I was never to find out. I had barely adjusted to the fact that there were not one but two lesbians in Edinburgh, when Mary's man burst into the room. He was a weel-kent Scottish poet. He said some unfriendly words as he reclaimed his property. Mary let herself be hustled away like an obedient little dog. I had already asked her to call on me the next evening, but of course she never arrived. The coffee remained simmering, the bottle of wine unopened. What became of you, Mary? Did you marry your hairy minstrel? You are probably a grandmother by now. The other two gay women, who were lovers, I met shortly before we all quitted Edinburgh. I departed for London and they went to China. We left for seemingly opposite reasons that were really the same reason.

They felt they were too conspicuous, and I felt that I did not exist. There was no place or community for us in Scotland.

The last twenty years have helped me understand the diversity of ways in which people experience gayness and also how long it can take to come to terms with it. My circumstances were unique to me; but they had something in common with those of all gay people of my generation. We were conditioned to accept our fragmented, twilight world. We were half-invisible to ourselves as well as to heterosexual society.

It is right to be concerned that Clause 28/29 offers a threat to our hard-won liberties. The effects of the legislation are particularly serious for young gays, who may have to struggle towards the homosexual community through barriers of isolation and self-hatred. Yet for most of us — and the young, too, if they can make it — it can never again be so bad as it was in the Fifties. We have become visible to ourselves and each other, as well as to the general public who are now aware that we exist in large numbers. When word is out, that can bring its own problems; but the worst oppression is self-oppression.

The Wabe

Peter D. Robinson

The wind snapped at his ankles as the dark carnivorous mouth of the pub closed smoked-glass lips behind him. Turning up his collar against the November night, David climbed the hill under the wholesome light of the moon which retreated every forty yards behind the jaundiced reach of the streetlamps. As he lowered himself into their car — his car — he made a conscious effort not to open the passenger door. Five years of habit is not easy to break; painful to have broken.

Driving up the motorway, David thought about the pub. Its dimly lit corners where couples sat cocooned in false privacy under the eyes of sad, voyeuristic old men. He thought of the pillars from where the hunters selected and then stalked their prey. Where music pulsed deathlessly into the smoke-filled air, mingling with the scent of Leather and Paco Rabanne. A bitter smile creased his face as he mentally re-ran the evening. On one hand, there were the faces he didn't know, some of whom were showing interest, indeed one had made an indifferent attempt at conversation, but he really couldn't drag up much enthusiasm for simultaneously pouring out their respective life histories, desperately seeking a common interest which could legitimise the 'coffee or something' question. On the other hand were the people he knew, the 'friends' who turned their faces away. They didn't want to talk. It was still too soon. It is always too soon to die! Far too bloody soon when your lover dies with you holding his hand to your face so that he, blind eighty-year-old incarcerated in a young man's body, can feel the tears you cry for him, for yourself, and for the doctors who told you in their ignorance that you had another year together.

That last time in hospital had been the best and the worst of it. Best because of Janet. Janet. A young, beautiful, strong nurse, humanely efficient, but with the herculean ability to shield from him the anxiety in her dusky eyes. Janet, whose jokes about night-sweats and bed-baths shouldn't have been funny, but were hilarious to them, vainly seeking a funny side to those most painful days: worst because the date and conditions for his return home changed almost daily and gradually receded into the fantasy world of the vaccine and the miracle drug. Towards the end even Janet ran out of one-liners as he ran out of time.

Even now David's mind ran with the hieroglyphic vocabulary of the disease: lymphocytes, pathogens, antigens, humoral and cellular immune responses, the non-functioning inner medullary space in the cortex of the lymph nodes, the opsonisation (or lack of it) by the dendritic macrophages of the pulp cords, twas brillig and the slithy toves did gire and gimble in the wabe. If ever he needed to give a lecture to the Boy Scouts on histology he wouldn't have to consult Gray's *Anatomy*. Ironic that one who felt nauseous to the point of collapse at the mention, never mind the sight of blood, and who had once fainted over the phone while making a dental appointment, should have spent two years drinking in everything he could read about bacteria, viruses, fungi, and multicellular parasites.

When he had been in Brussels and his 'other' had gone out on his blind date with destiny, David nightly sent a kiss through the air and did his best to hug the empty space beside him. Strange that for all the power of imagination, you can never recreate the touch, the physical contact between yourself and another. You would think that the nerve ends would remember what it is like to touch, but they don't. So while he lay touching himself in an effort to jog their memory, his other had welcomed into his body its tiny executioner. Not that there were any recriminations (spilt milk and all that). Anyway, each TV broadcast lengthened the dormant stage after exposure to the virus, so who could say for sure when it happened. They needed a scapegoat, however. A date. An act. The Brussels trip was as good as any. He had asked David to forgive him. Can you forgive someone for committing the sin which will tear you apart? It is either too foolish to consider, or beyond the limits of magnanimity. David realised that the car had stopped moving. Patting the steering-wheel, he thanked George, the auto-pilot of his subconscious, for getting him back safely and went reluctantly into the home which cried out for togetherness but found only half of together, which is alone.

A week later and he was back in the pub where each sought their Adonis and found only Narcissus. Just the experience of being in a place where everyone was like him; where the men loved men, and the women only women, gave him strength. He laved his soul in that elusive feeling of belonging even as he swore that this was a 'one drink and away' occasion. Later, he could never say when it was that the contact was made, he simply became aware that they were smiling at each other. The blond hair and almost white eyebrows, of which one was raised expectantly, were sufficiently contrary to his 'type' to warrant pursuit of the quarry, if only to conclude after the chase that he didn't want to follow the hunt to its logical conclusion.

They talked. Who remembers what is said in that first frenzied communication, as each tries to transmit their validity, their worth as a catch, to the other? They talked of summer (which was far away), of Paris (which was farther), of friends (who were being ignored), and they talked of sex, which was fast becoming an almost tangible current flowing between them. Eventually they spoke of everything and anything (even politics, which for David was unheard of), rather than be forced into the situation where they would have to fully say hello or really goodbye. David remarked on a modern paraphrase of the courtly style: 'The exquisite agony of sexual frustration which far outweighs the smoking of the post-coital cigarette.' They both laughed at that though neither of them smoked. Still laughing, they left the pub.

Half an hour's torrid conversation hardly qualified them to be called a couple, rather, two individuals, soldered without flux by need as much as desire.

Afterwards, when eventually the heartbeats had slowed, and the breathing relaxed, they talked again. This time it was less frantic. You don't need to impress someone whose sweat has mingled with your own. Intimacy of that kind, like noticing that he buys his underwear from Marks and Spencers too, removes all the barriers to conversation. So Andrew talked of his divorce, his kids, and his coming out, and David spoke of his coming out, his work, and, yes, of his dead lover. Somehow he felt it was all right, knew that he was at last being purged of the anger and at least the worst of the pain. 'Y'know,' he said, 'we slept together for five years. Safe sex? Didn't come into it. And I'm still fucking negative!' Things were a touch awkward then, for a bit, but a little more of what the pamphlets unimaginatively called body rubbing soothed the friction.

Over the months the need and desire for socialising apart diminished. One car took them everywhere while the other sulked in the garage. Even the two flats seemed not so much an extravagance, rather, one was becoming superfluous. They phoned the building society and asked for some bumpf on non-marital joint mortgages. Before return of post, Reality intervened. Andrew caught a cold, which developed into pneumonia and the bells started ringing in David's head. Sanity disintegrated in a rush of memories, and security slipped from their fingers via the phone call from the clinic which announced that an irregularity had been found in Andrew's blood. Irregularity! Why could they not be honest and say that the death warrant had been signed and sealed, and only awaited delivery? 'Something to do with helper-T cells,' Andrew said. David explained. He even managed a wry smile as he thought that at least his knowledge wasn't going to waste.

Test followed test, and slowly the mortar binding their lives together began to be washed away under the tide of waiting rooms and *Punch* magazines. They made running repairs as they went; a night at the theatre here, a new Billie Holliday album there, but it was a bit like putting a sticking plaster over an arterial fissure. The damage was done and no amount of cosmetic camouflage would dismiss it.

It was eventually discovered that Andrew's pneumonia had been only that: he was still positive, but the pneumonia had been the whole disease not just one symptom of a greater one. For all the shiny young doctor knew, Andrew could be one of the lucky one's who have the virus but never develop the disease. 'Or haven't yet,' he added, shattering what little false hope they had allowed themselves.

Life went on. Not as normal; normal is not a word which sits easily with either Gays or AIDS, but it went on. David felt as though he had opened Life's binnacle only to find it empty. He intercepted the letter from the building society and slipped it under the mattress in the spare room. Andrew either guessed, or found it, or both, because he never once mentioned mortgages, who had been so keen at the outset. For weeks equilibrium returned — no one broke any mirrors anyway. Then David started having dreams, or rather had the same dream again and again.

He sat at the big kitchen table swinging his legs idly, stopping now and again to examine the scab on his knee. The worrying of this latest trophy caused him such a pleasurable pain, despite his mother's warning that if he played with it, it would never heal. His mother, a combination of woollens and silks, smells of baking and birthday scent, comforting softness and cutting scorn, came into the room and seeing David's idleness, immediately thought of something for him to do before the devil should. 'Will you go and get the eggs, Davey boy?' she asked in a tone which brooked neither refusal nor evasion. David rose with one last, successful tweak at his knee. The scab tore free and the comforting trickle of warmth wound its crimson way down his bare shin. He put on his duffel-coat, doing up the toggles with both hands. (He had never perfected the 'one-handed toggle-twist' as his elder brothers were quick to remind him.) He lifted the latch on the scullery door. 'Wellies!' boomed the voice of doom. (In his more philosophical moments David had come to the conclusion that adults had been placed on earth with the sole purpose of preventing children from getting dirty and thence enjoying themselves.) Once his wellies, and the required socks for padding, were on, David emerged from the industrious warmth of the kitchen into the sharpness of the morning.

The grey sky glared down on him as if it resented his intrusion. Half-closing his eyes against the light's indignation, he began to cross the yard. By some caprice of nature, large stretches of the ground were bone-dry while a few paces away lay inviting, gloriously adhesive pools of mud. Daffodils fought for nutrients as the hens battled for grain. Scattering before his approach, these chickens regrouped, fluffing and rearranging their dignity, crying out at the impudence of this two-leg.

A motley collection of old doors, warped planks and metal sheeting, the hen-house stood dejectedly in the middle of the yard. David approached quietly; the secret was not to alarm the layers — a frightened hen wouldn't lay, and while to his mother fewer eggs meant less to sell to the village shop, to David it meant spam sandwiches to take to school, something to be avoided at all costs. He entered silently, or as silently as one can open a door with creaking, rusty hinges and step on scattered old, dry straw.

The warmth and cooing contentment of the shadows welcomed David, but he had to shut his eyes for a moment to let them become accustomed to the gloom. He lifted a big Red from her stall and she clucked boastfully as he gently took up the alabastrine product of her womb. The egg shattered at his touch. He discarded it and wiped his hands free of the glutinous substance. Gingerly, with breath held, he lifted another egg. He almost managed to put it safely in his duffel-coat pocket before it crumpled in his hand. And so it went on. No matter how gentle he was, no matter how carefully he raised the eggs from their straw cushions, they shattered messily in his fingers. David woke trying vainly to wipe the viscous fluid from his hands like some latter-day Lady Macbeth.

When did the dream become reality? Gradually the fabric of their relationship came apart at the seams. Instead of riding out difficult patches with as much tolerance and understanding as he could muster, David's patience evaporated, and he would wade in with all guns blazing. Instead of saying 'Okay honey, let's see what we can do about this', it was 'It seems, Andrew, as if you are the one with the problem here'. The washing was thrown into the machine with a curse rather than the smile it used to get as he thought of the wearer of half the pile. He caught himself a couple of times on the phone, bitching about Andrew. That they had agreed to keep their troubles private, didn't seem to matter anymore.

Making love became having sex. Having sex became a chore. David tried to re-weave the magic: candles, a special meal, good wine; but the result was sex, not love. Formerly unimportant things began to take on new titanic significance. David's habit of idly flicking through the teletext pages while they watched television, Andrew's tendency to replace empty biscuit wrappers in the tin, these and others like them became the death throes of their relationship, which had once been the foibles of their love. They had played their hands well with the few aces they had been dealt, but David was fast losing his taste for the game. Simply wearing the same brand of underwear is no basis for a relationship. Or was that just an excuse? Was he not really just trying to get out, before he had to go through all the pain again? It wasn't really Andrew. Andrew was confused and hurting just as much as he. David didn't want to have to meet another Janet, didn't want to be left again as that half of together which is alone.

Elijah and Isaac

John McRae

Isaac and Elijah
Were a beautiful couple.
Lived in Jackson, Mississippi.
We met them: Went to see
Dressed to Kill

Loved it

Went home. Ate
Creole,
Made love.

Kept in touch
Three years.

This June Elijah died of AIDS.
This is not a poem about Elijah dying of AIDS.
I love the memory of him.

But God I weep for Isaac.

published in Not Love Alone *(GMP, 1985) and used in AIDS benefits worldwide*

A Scottish Childhood Now

John McRae

Between the lines
Of how it happened
And how it's told

Lies the distance
That turns to gold

Or becomes the cold
Of growing no younger
While not growing old.

Return to memory
and a long-lost land
of childhood summers
and love's sweet hand
a lost romance
of sex unplanned

Make me disguise Dalguise
And meld Dunkeld
Into realms of gold
To keep out the cold

Of how lies the land
And how closed the fold

Between how it happened
And how it's told.

A Bad Landing

John McRae

Coming in to Lafayette
letters and a number on the glass
inside the window, with the date
September 1970
when we first met,
told me this plane was built
as our love was born.

Coming into Lafayette
a thunderstorm and violent winds
made the plane as vulnerable
as love,
and my heart lurched
in fear for love
and ending all together.

A Preface to John Henry Mackay

HUBERT KENNEDY

KNOWN to the public as a lyric poet, novelist, and anarchist propagandist, John Henry Mackay was also the first to try to organise his fellow boy-lovers in order to gain acceptance of the right of men and boys to love one another. He gave his considerable talent and the 'best years' of his life, as he said, to his literary campaign under the pseudonym Sagitta. Refusing to accept defeat when his early pamphlets were legally declared immoral in 1909, he continued his writing and distributed his 'Books of the Nameless Love' underground. They are a precious legacy from the early years of our movement.

Son of a Scots father, the marine insurance broker John Farquhar Mackay, and a German mother, Louise Auguste Mackay née Ehlers, John Henry Mackay was born in Greenock on 8 February 1864 and so was only nineteen months old when his father died there on 11 September 1865. His mother then took him back with her to Germany, where she later remarried. Thus Mackay grew up with German as his mother tongue. He later learned to speak and read English — but never wrote it well.

After leaving school Mackay was an apprentice in a publishing house for a year and then a university student for five semesters in Kiel, Leipzig and Berlin. He never earned a degree, but an allowance from his mother gave him the financial independence to devote himself to a career as writer. His first publication followed a visit to Scotland in August and September of 1885, when he called on relatives and visited Edinburgh and the Western Isles. The result, *Die Kinder des Hochlands* (Children of the Highlands), an imitation of the narrative poetry of Walter Scott,[1] is set on Mull and extolls the beauties of this island. Instant fame came to him, however, with the publication in 1891 of *Die Anarchisten* (The Anarchists), which was published in English that same year by Mackay's American friend Benjamin R. Tucker, in Boston. By 1910 there were translations into six other languages, including a Yiddish version published in London. The book is based on the year that Mackay spent in London in 1887-1888 and describes events of that Jubilee Year, especially as they touched on the lives of the socialist and anarchist German exiles there. The central character presents the case for Mackay's individualist anarchism.

By 1888, when his biography of Max Stirner appeared, Mackay was also known as the rediscoverer of that philosopher of egoism. While visiting Berlin the composer Richard Strauss wrote to his father on 7 April 1892: 'In Berlin I made an engaging new acquaintance, the Scottish poet John Henry Mackay, a great anarchist and biographer of the Berlin philosopher Max Stirner.'[2] Strauss later set four of Mackay's lyrics to music and two of them 'Morgen' (Tomorrow) and 'Heimliche Aufforderung' (Secret Invitation), are among his most popular songs. Several other composers also set Mackay lyrics, including Eugen d'Albert, who was born in Glasgow on 10 April 1864. (He died in Riga, Latvia, 3 March 1932.)

The death of Mackay's mother in 1902 brought on a depression from which he was delivered only by his dedication to his new cause, that of championing 'the nameless love', as he called it. The poem with that title was one of four published under the pseudonym Sagitta in 1905 in the Berlin gay journal *Der Eigene,* which had begun in 1896 as an anarchist journal in the direction of Max Stirner (reflected in the title: der Eigene equals self-owner, in the meaning given that word by Stirner), but from 1898 was openly homosexual. Because of the prosecution of his early pamphlets the complete edition of the 'Books of Nameless Love' could only be sold underground and did not appear until 1913. This included the short autobiographical novel *Fenny Skaller,* which a friend of Mackay called his 'confessions of life and love'.[3] In the novel, the central character, Fenny Skaller, has waited in vain for a new young acquaintance to keep an appointment. Disappointed, he returns to his rooms and consoles himself by looking through his collection of photographs of ten boys he has loved. His life is then recalled in flashback in the ten chapters, called 'pictures'. The friendship described in 'The Second Picture' also appears, less explicitly, in Mackay's *Der Freiheitsucher* (The Freedomseeker) and is surely based on personal experience.

Mackay did not return to Scotland after 1885 and there is little evidence that he thought of himself as a Scot, except in a very conventional, stereotypical way. For example, in discussing his plan to publish *Der Freitheitsucher* shortly after the First World War he wrote to Benjamin R. Tucker (in English, for Tucker did not read German): 'The prices for printing and paper here are abominable, and I am not sure yet, if I can fulfill my plan. But you know, what an awful Scotch thick-head I am, and that I never give up a thing, before I do not see the absolute impossibility.'[4] Still, he was not naturalised in Germany until around 1900, after he decided to settle permanently in Berlin. And Mackay's

German biographer, Kurt Zube, who knew him personally, recalled an occasion when an irritating example of German servility caused Mackay to say: 'I am not a German; I am a Scotchman!'[5]

Mackay's financial situation worsened following the war, especially after the runaway inflation wiped out the value of the annuity he had purchased with money left him by his mother, so that in his later years he was completely dependent on the sale of his books, which never regained their earlier popularity. Mackay died in Berlin on 16 May 1933, just six days after the infamous burning of books of 'un-German spirit' by the Nazis. Some of his books were probably in that bonfire; all of his Sagitta writings were later on the Nazi list of forbidden books. That they can now be reprinted is a confirmation of his final optimism when he wrote: 'They murder our love — and it lives. They strangle our cry — and it echoes back from the future. They have murdered my books. But my books will live.'[6]

Footnotes

1. Edward Mornin, 'A Late German Imitation of Walter Scott', *Germanic Notes* 17 (1986): 49–51.
2. Willi Schuh, *Richard Strauss: a chronicle of the early years 1864–1898*, translated by Mary Whittall (Cambridge: Cambridge University Press, 1982), p. 258.
3. Friedrich Dobe, *John Henry Mackay als Mensch* (Koblenz: Edition Plato, 1987), p. 60.
4. Mackay to Tucker, 22 February 1920, Benjamin R. Tucker Papers, New York Public Library, New York.
5. Kurt Zube [K. H. Z. Solman], *Der Bahnbrecher John Henry Mackay: Sein Leben und Sein Werk* (Freiburg/Br.: Verlag der Mackay Gesellschaft, 1979), p. 101.
6. John Henry Mackay, *Fenny Skaller and other Prose Writings from the Books of the Nameless Love*, translated by Hubert Kennedy (Amsterdam: Southernwood Press, 1988), p. 155.

The Second Picture

John Henry Mackay

He looked for the second picture, found it in one glance, and the blood shot hot to his heart. The small, pale and unreal shadow disappeared into its nothingness before the life that, with its desires, now sprang into the plot on both feet and demanded its right.

He, whose picture Skaller now held in his hand, *he* had been his first love, his first love and his first passion! From the first day on, when they had met on the wide steps of the strange school, they had loved one another until the last, when they left this school, never to see one another again; and they never knew that their friendship was love, their love passion. What more did they know of life than that it was life? They had loved one another with all the wonderful signs of love: tender and violent at the same time, obstinate and shy, fearful and joyful, jealous and watchful. They did not reflect that they were young, they did not know that they were beautiful. The had not the least idea that their love was a crime in people's eyes.

They loved one another. They dreamed together their first dream of life: of its glories and its fame, of the life that lay beyond the prison walls of this school and beyond this miserable town, which to despise was their delight, of the life that must open up soon before them, that was only waiting for the two of them in order to receive them and shower them with its infinite gifts!

The picture began to tremble in the hand that held it.

How handsome he had been, his first friend! How soft the cheeks, how shining the eyes, how full the lips! It seemed to Skaller as if he must kiss them again, those lips. But he only bent deeper over the picture.

It had lost none of its splendour, as old as it was, as little as had his memory. For Skaller saw everything again, as it had been then twenty-five years ago, as clearly as if it had been yesterday. In unheard-of clarity, the words that had been spoken returned, the glances that had been exchanged. What foolishness, what extravagance, what mistakes! And yet: how full of life everything was, as it was full of fervour and fierce desire, and therefore — how genuine and true it all was!

He, Fenny, sixteen, and the other, a year younger, Gustav — there must also be another picture, which shows the two of them together: it was there already. There they stood beside one another — two proper boys in their school caps and ill-fitting suits, somewhat comical in the early self-consciousness of those years, but still charming in their vitality.

Skaller looked into his own face. Had he also been so serious already at that time? And it occurred to him that it had almost always been like that: he the serious and thoughtful one, and the one he loved mostly careless and unconcerned. Again the blood shot quickly to his heart.

He laid the picture down and seated himself before the table. He covered his eyes with both hands and walked the path of his life backwards, back to its first source, and was again young, quite young.

Clearly to be grasped with all his senses, he suddenly saw

again the scenes of his happiness, his first, great, boundless happiness.

*

'Fenny! Fenny!' the boys shout. He should play with them. For they all like him. In spite of his being so serious. But he already no longer hears them.

On paths that only he knows, he walks around the small town with the large school, leaves it behind him, and steals past the shouts up to the wooded hills.

Here is their 'nest'. No path leads to it. But he knows the way.

He bends branches apart, slips through under them, slides over the carpet of moss — in the depth of the night he would know where he was going. He has reached it. He is the first today.

It is truly a 'nest'. They have built it under hanging branches, here in the middle of the forest: they dug a deep hole, propped it with boards that they secretly and with immense effort dragged here, and buried their treasures under the thick cover of moss. A covering of green arched over it, so thick that no rain came through.

He goes to work. Carefully he raises the cover of fern and moss from the hole, and takes out what they hide: books, candy, and smoking tobacco, protected against moisture in leaden boxes. Then he cleans the bed of needles and berries, spreads an old blanket over it, stretches himself at length, his hands folded under his head, and looks through the branches at what he can see of the blue sky.

He is waiting for his friend.

Bugs creep around him through the tendrils and quite near a thrush is singing. He waits. His heart beats faster and once a trembling goes through his slender body like unbearable expectation.

He turns around and listens. With all his might. For from below there sounds the cracking of twigs. And then: another sound, like a light whistle.

No doubt: it is he! But he remains lying. Only from his lips cautiously comes the same answer.

The breaking of twigs becomes louder and comes nearer and nearer. Then the branches are quickly thrown apart and his friend stands before him, deep red and out of breath. His short pants have shoved up over the bare knees and one shows bloody scratches. He throws himself without a word onto the blanket beside him. He is unable to speak, he is so out of breath. Then little by little words are exchanged. They wanted to keep Gustav back too and he had to free himself.

Now they have eaten and drunk, taking turns from their one glass with the broken pedestal, smoked their short pipe, and are finally done telling their experiences of the past day. They lie mutely beside one another. Without knowing it, they have drawn quite close together.

There is a damp and oppressive sultriness under the thick, leafy canopy. The thrush, near them in the crown of a beech, is still singing, and in the town below the tower clock strikes. They count the strokes: six.

The silence between them becomes ever more uneasy. They both have the same thought: Who will begin today? And each knows what the other is thinking.

Then the older one bends over the younger and kisses him on the lips, hastily and shyly. And suddenly they embrace, both at the same time, quickly and impetuously.

*

In the chair before his desk, on which the pictures lay, Skaller was sitting with his hands in front of his eyes.

Fenny! Fenny! Thus the boys had shouted.

Fenny — so he had been named once: by his mother, his family, his playmates. He had been christened Ferdinand: Ferdinand Skaller. But he was called Fenny by those who loved him. He was called Fenny . . .

By whom else yet?

He started. Abruptly. Where had he been? And what had so aroused him?

A picture lay close in front of him. Again he picked it up.

How beautiful it was, this young face! How wonderfully beautiful it had been!

Had been!

He was again conscious of where he was: in the room of his own apartment, on the third floor of a large house, he was sitting on this Sunday afternoon, an ageing man, old not in years, but in their disappointments.

Yes, life had come, but not as they had dreamed it, as the great liberator from restraint and narrowness, but rather as the great enemy, with which he had to fight, fight as he was still fighting today and must fight until the end, with never the hope of victory!

Murderers, not warriors, had been sent against him, and he himself had paid these murderers with his own blood. This very day he would have to look these murderers in the face, the murderers of his youth!

It had not been as he had dreamed at that time with the beloved of his youth: fame and glory, honour and victory. Rather stupidity and cowardice, fear and difficult self-control. But finally there was a victory, a quiet one in his own breast, and something like the elevation of disdain over stupidity and meanness, and rest after the long battle.

Once again Skaller picked up the two pictures, but only the features of the other boy still held his glance. Where was he today? They had continued to write, frequently at first, then more and more seldom, and only once more had he heard from him, by chance, after long years: married, a father, in a high judicial position. Skaller smiled bitterly: surely he sentenced, had to sentence those who were dragged before him because of this love, for the sake of this same love with which he himself once loved — of which he knew nothing more today — which he had forgotten — or which he thought of yet only as an aberration of his youth.

But he, Skaller, had never forgotten it. For him, it was still today what it had been then: the first love of his life and his first, great passion! Yes, much more than that even: the only love of his young life that had come as love must come — uncalled and overpowering, without the sequel of second thoughts, without the burden of regret. And beautiful: played over by the cheerful light of young and strong vigour, entirely desire of the senses and entirely pleasure in one another. Love, which indeed hid itself, but not shyly and fearfully, rather secretly and thoughtfully, so as not to be touched by a stranger's hand — his first love, not his strongest and certainly not his deepest, but surely his most blessed.

As he laid the two pictures aside with the first one he felt that it was a farewell — a farewell to his youth, his youth and the greatest happiness that this youth had given him.

translated from the German by Hubert Kennedy

The Woman She Came to Seek

Sigrid Nielsen

Jean de Vaubrun rode to Edinburgh from France in the autumn of 1792 [or possibly 1793], never pausing in his search for the woman he loved. Here I shall find you, Céline, soul of my soul, he told the summits of Arthur's Seat as they rose into view over the flats of Dunbar.

[How far away could you really see bloody Arthur's Seat? On the train journey, it came up somewhere near the Prestonpans Power Station, but it was no use trying to mention that.]

His horsemanship was superb. His clothes clung to his tall, slender frame, though they were slightly mussed after being slept in for a week. He had shared a bed in the mean inns along the way and preferred not to let anyone know he was a woman. He took out his watch in its battered silver case with Liberté, Égalité, Fraternité engraved inside the cover, framing Céline's perfect features and commanding dark eyes . . .

*

'D'you go out in the evening?' asked Patrice McKechnie.

Catriona started to say 'Not a lot', in a sort of hard, youth-of-today voice. She used it with people who didn't know her very well. Now, however, it struck her that she'd better not give Patrice an opening, though she wasn't quite sure why.

'I work on my novel,' she said.

'Oh,' said Patrice.

'It's about the French Revolution.'

'You're no bad looking,' said Patrice.

'Ta very much,' said Catriona, deadpan.

'I mean it.'

Catriona's brain was jamming. 'Red hair,' said Patrice, taking a hank of Catriona's very long and kinky hair in her hand. 'Means you're passionate.' She grinned. 'Ooh, there's my order up. Can you give that lot on 2b coffee, hen? The table in the corner. Ta. If you're no busy.'

'I'm no busy,' said Catriona.

*

Dark flakes of snow tumbled past the candlelit windows of the Countess of Ratho's townhouse in Charlotte Square. The granite steps and the pillared doorcase were new and unmarked by the city's dirty air. Jean, elegant in his cloak and three-cornered hat, strode up and put his hand on the cold brass door-knocker . . .

[Except that it wasn't snowing, because this has to have been November. Because Jean was fleeing from the September Massacres. Unless they didn't actually happen in September. The book's away to the library. Oh, who cares.]

'I've been waiting for you,' said the Countess. She had a soirée known as the Cercle Republicain. Jean handed his cloak to the liveried servant, who bowed. His gaze met the intelligent green eyes of the Countess, eyes whose expression had all the warmth and silent wilfulness of her native land. Jean looked at her a moment too long, then forced himself to gaze over her shoulder to the well-tailored figures among the candelabra. It was not going to be simple, finding Céline . . .

*

'It's my cousin,' said Patrice.

'I see,' said Catriona.

'He's a mate of my husband's. You'd like him. He's doing the business course at Stevenson College. We're all going out on Saturday night —'

Even when you knew you were going to blush, thought Catriona, you could never do anything about it. And it was one thing to lie, and another to blush. Blushing suggested you weren't just lying, but that you had something to hide. What Catriona had to hide was that she hated turning down any gift from Patrice, who was the best waitress in the place, as well as the nicest. Catriona liked having someone to trade silly remarks with at the staff table, and to say 'safe home' when she walked back to her bedsitter after the evening shift. Patrice was an impulsive, on-or-off sort of person. She wouldn't ask twice.

Have to visit my mum at the weekend, thought Catriona. An honest lie, not one of your wee slippery round-the-corner-from-the-truth excuses with nervous grins on their faces.

'Catriona,' said Rose-Marie, 'that's your turkey cérise on the counter for the last five minutes.' Rose-Marie, part owner of the Right and Wrong Restaurant, was a former model from Toulon in the south of France. Napoleon had fought one of his early battles at Toulon, but Rose-Marie hadn't realised this until Catriona pointed it out.

'This is a going concern!' said Rose-Marie. 'We're not here for glamour.'

'Sorry,' said Catriona. Patrice pretended not to have heard. 'What about —' she began, but Catriona grabbed the moment to escape to the kitchen with an amiably wretched smile on her face.

'Patreese,' said Rose-Marie, 'there's a new girl coming in tonight. I want you to show her the ropes. She has a lot of energy, uh-huh? I know she'll work out and be very, very good. Not like some of these slack people. The Scottish aren't lazy like the English. I don't care what anybody says.'

*

Dear Anne,

I've had a job now for about a month. It's in the High Street in a restaurant that's named after the old Right and Wrong Club in Edinburgh. The point of the Right and Wrong Club was to see if you could get guttered six nights a week and not a lot has changed. All the doors have fanlights even though they are in the basement. We do crèpes Flambées and lobster thermidor. The menu says the lobster is flown in every day from South Africa.

I write every afternoon between shifts. The story is getting quite exciting. Céline has escaped from the Marquis de Pierre-Noire and fled to Edinburgh. I plan to be finished in 18 months or so. The only problem is that I'm tired sometimes and write more or less whatever comes into my head. I still can't make up my mind what exactly to do about trying to get a university place or something like it, and I would feel better, I think, if we could talk about what you said when I visited you. I'm sorry I haven't written since then, but I've felt very confused about some things that happened with us and you didn't seem to want to say any more. I mean, that may have been the right impression, and I don't want to force you to say more than you want to, or really anything, but I'd like to know if you still want to write to me, possibly just about books, or if you wanted to —

*

'When I met you in Paris,' said Mme de Ratho, 'I wanted to say —'

'Citizen Vaubrun!'

It was a familiar voice, but not, Jean realised with a start, the voice he thought he had heard. With a shock of disappointment he recognised Livée de St-Orages, another republican refugee like himself, whose background was no longer humble enough for the government. Livée played the spinet and was one of the few women in France to have mastered the analytical geometry of René Descartes.

'Livée, perhaps you can be of some help to Citizen Vaubrun,' said Mme de Ratho pointedly. 'He is searching for another refugee. Perhaps you have heard of her?'

'Edinburgh is packed with refugees these days.'

'He is looking for Mademoiselle Céline de Mont-Mercure.'

'Surely not . . . the Duchesse de Mont-Mercure.'

'She has renounced her title,' said Jean firmly. He had no sense of telling a lie; after all, Céline must surely have realised that she was forfeiting her title by fleeing to Scotland.

'Alas! I have not heard of her,' said Livée wistfully. 'I fear I cannot help you. I am desolated.'

'Come, Citizen Vaubrun,' said Mme de Ratho, 'there is someone over here I want you to meet . . .'

*

Dear Anne,

How is your course going? I'm sure I know the answer to that anyway. I saw your mum when I was visiting my parents in Greylaw a couple of months ago. She said you were interning with a stockbroker and it was a special summer programme, so all the best and all the rest everyone else has already said to you. Your mum said you weren't liking the Smoke much better but that it was alright. So here I am in Edinburgh, same old place, thinking I might as well write and say hi ya . . .

Catriona didn't send that letter either.

*

'There's someone over here I want you to meet,' said Patrice.

Catriona's eyes raked the room for the cousin, but the bar and the more downmarket tables were empty.

'No over there, over here. The new lass.'

'Oh.'

'Sarah Donahue.'

'Hullo,' said Catriona, hoping she didn't sound too relieved. But she did. She realised she sounded elated.

Sarah was shorter than Catriona, and she had straight reddish hair, not the wild and curly type. Her eyes were a washed-out blue with a level gaze. She wore no make-up and no rings on her freckly hands.

'Hi,' she said.

'Sarah's from America,' said Patrice.

'I'm just here for the summer,' said Sarah.

'It's spring,' said Catriona stupidly.

'It's almost summer,' said Sarah, obviously not put off.

'Catriona's a writer,' said Patrice.

'I usedta know some writers,' said Sarah, leaving no doubt she could handle the experience.

Later, at the staff table, Sarah told Catriona and Patrice that she was from New York and that she and her mother were travelling around Europe. Her mother was doing a study of unemployment for an American government department. 'She'll be with us yet awhile, then,' said Patrice with a sour laugh. Sarah lit up a fag. Catriona decided not to mention that she hated cigarette smoke. Somebody left a half carafe of house red, probably with good reason, but they all downed it while Rose-Marie was in the kitchen arguing with her husband. 'Thought you hated wine, Kate,' said Dougie the table-clearer. 'I hate being called Kate,' said Catriona in Jean's accent, flicking her fingers and pouting, which inspired a rash of imitations of Rose-Marie and the French in general. They all had to wipe the smiles off their faces when she came striding through the door.

*

Great longing, thought Jean, has its uses. Great longing sets the mind free of concern for trivialities. Great longing leaves the soul free to feel clearly and spurs the imagination to create what is most truly desired.

In the short space of time it took him to walk across the room arm-in-arm with Mme de Ratho, he thought he saw . . . Could it be? She stood in the doorway with her hand on her hip as she always did when she was angry. Her dark hair fell loose in ringlets, in the fashion of the time. She was dressed in brilliant white, in a simple gown and satin slippers. A fichu of the finest Valenciennes lace covered her neck and shoulders. 'Jean,' she cried, her eyes blazing, 'why in God's name didn't you write?'

At the sound of her voice Jean started forward. 'Is something wrong?' asked Mme de Ratho. His heart pounding, Jean looked at the door. A different woman stood there, a meagre little woman of twenty-eight or nine or even older. His imagination had created it all. How powerful I am, he thought. How powerful! How helpless!

*

'This way,' said Sarah.

'Where?'

'If I don't have a smoke I'll crack.'

'Isn't that Rose-Marie's garden?'

Sarah sniffed, or laughed, it was hard to tell which. She ran down the stairs and opened the glass door, and Catriona followed. They sat on a patch of wizened grass at the foot of a three-storey-high rose-bush.

'Whoo. Jesus. That's better.'

'What if she comes out here?'

'She and greasy Guy are doing an inventory on the wines.'

The garden wall and the towering backs of the High Street tenements were catching the sun. It was almost warm: Edinburgh was having its two weeks of summer. It would be mid-June soon. Anne would be finishing her term.

'Besides,' said Sarah, 'didn't you notice her eyes?' She may take quite a while adding up the wine list.'

'She did tell me she has sensitive eyes. That's why she always wears tinted spectacles.'

'Looks like pot. But it might be coke.'

Catriona had already laughed when she realised it wasn't a joke.

'I suppose you're very experienced,' she said apologetically, but Sarah took it as a question.

'Well, at my age, I ought to be.'

'At your age?'

'Thirty.' Sarah held her ringless hand up to take another drag.

'You're really thirty,' said Catriona, trying to sound as if she were pretending she didn't believe it.

'And I'm not married,' said Sarah. 'Isn't that the next question?'

'No — I mean —'

'I was engaged. But he gave me a hard time. So one day

I poured a cup of coffee over his head. I think he took it personally.' She grinned.

Catriona's mind was spinning. She felt she ought to write Sarah a very simple and sincere and official letter of thanks for not being married. She had never known any woman who had survived to the age of thirty unmarried without developing a severe case of flower-patterned blouses and low-heeled blue-grey shoes.

She looked at Sarah's face. Sarah didn't seem to mind. Sarah's skin might be thirty (except that Catriona had never tried to judge the age of anyone's skin before). But it made no difference. Sarah's face was young.

It was not until a long time afterwards that Catriona thought she understood the reason Sarah seemed young, which was simple: she looked directly at everyone and let them look back at her. She even let the school-leavers who washed the dishes and cleared the tables look straight into her eyes. Most older people never invited such a thing; most younger people never dared to do it.

That day, however, Catriona thought it was Sarah's eyes and her mouth which were young. She noticed Sarah's chapped lips. Sarah's face was bony (as well as freckly), but her lips were rather full. She had a nice mouth, almost a kind mouth.

Sarah stubbed out her cigarette at the foot of Rose-Marie's rose-bush, stood up, and studied the round black mark with satisfaction.

'Who could've put that there? Did you see anything?'

'No,' said Catriona.

*

'My oldest friend,' said Mme de Ratho. 'You must meet her. We shared a room at convent school. We were lonely together.

We suffered the barbarities of the school régime and swore to live free for the rest of our lives!'

Jean swept a graceful but careless bow. Sarah van Williamsburgh, of the new American republic, smiled as she took in his fiery hair, strong regular features, and green eyes.

'I'm glad to see that the cause of freedom has acquired such energetic support in Edinburgh,' she said.

Jean took a deep breath. In the course of filling his lungs he felt as if he were rising a few inches off the ground. He also remembered that he had a secret, though, at that moment, he could not quite recall what it was.

*

'Look at this,' said Sarah the next day.

They were together in the big cupboard behind the staff room, refilling the sugar bowls. It was the magical hour after the lunch shift, when everyone had gone away and there was no sound louder than the hoover.

'Present from Alan behind the bar,' said Sarah, drawing out the glass she had been holding behind the frilly apron the waitresses at the Right and Wrong had to wear.

Catriona took a look at the brown liquid and thought, 'I'm nineteen years old, I've failed all my O-grades, and I'm a disgrace to my family. I think I can just about manage whisky.' She took the glass from Sarah.

'It's cognac.'

'The kind Napoleon liked,' said Catriona, wiping her eyes and pulling a face.

'Stop exaggerating. It's not that bad.'

'No, no, fine, fine,' said Catriona, faking a cough.

'Always sending yourself up. Innocent Scots lassie meets the big bad world.'

Catriona grinned. It was a painful grin. She had never

heard anyone make this kind of remark to another person's face before. It wasn't a compliment. But the fact that Sarah had said it at all seemed to mean she thought they were very close friends. Or was she just trying to make Catriona angry? Sarah seemed to have a special liking for angry gestures, even when she had provoked them herself.

'I expect you have to know someone quite well to say things like that,' said Catriona solemnly.

Sarah ignored her. 'Somebody should give you practise drinking your own whisky. I'm going to Mather's Bar on Friday night. You know where that is?'

'Yes, it's right on my way home.'

'Good. I don't know this place. You're going to have to get me there.'

Another flash was going off in Catriona's mind. A minute before, she had hated bars and drinking and what people called 'going out'; now she felt pleased and flattered, just as if Sarah had invited her to do something interesting. It was very odd. They finished filling the sugar bowls and Catriona left for the afternoon. She could taste the cognac all the way down the Mound.

*

Dear Mum,

I tried ringing, but you were out, and I can't ring in the evenings because I'm working. I expect I didn't get your message because people in the other bedsits sometimes forget to pass them on. Or they put them under the wrong door. Unfortunately, there is nothing to be done about this. I'm afraid I won't be able to make it back to Greylaw this weekend because I have promised to go out with the cousin of a friend. He is studying business management. He seems very nice. I think it would be rude to try to put him off now.

I hope you and Dad are well. The garden must be looking very nice. I expect you're busy with the ladies' altar guild and the old people's picnic. I will try to arrange things better another time.

Love,

Catriona

*

The clock chimed in the hall; as it stopped, Jean heard the faint sound of the bells drifting across the Old Town. He never noticed the hour. Mlle van Williamsburgh was sitting beside him in a corner of the study, by the fire. Far away across the room, her mother was deep in conversation with a handsome young advocate; they were discussing the merits of a written constitution.

'I fell in love with her the first time I saw her,' Jean was saying.

He was surprised to find himself speaking about Céline to Miss van Williamsburgh; but not deeply surprised. Ordinarily he would not have spoken of one woman to another, but Miss van Williamsburgh was so straightforward, so unaffected, and Céline was always so near the surface of his thoughts.

'You fell in love with her. And did she fall in love with you?'

'Yes,' said Jean. 'And we swore a pledge.'

'And what happened then?'

'Oh, quite a lot,' said Jean, who found it rather hard to explain the number of duels, pursuits on horseback, quick changes of identity and narrow escapes from the authorities he had experienced by the age of twenty-four. 'Her grandmother married her to a very royalist nobleman, and she ran away from him to Edinburgh.'

'And she sent you a message asking you to join her?'

'I would find here wherever she was. No matter what effort it might take.'

'But did she ask you to come here?'

'I'm not sure what you mean,' said Jean.

'She is a lady of means,' said Miss van Williamsburgh gently, 'and, from what you say, a lady of strong character.'

'Absolutely,' said Jean, whose lips and fingers tingled slightly at the opportunity to say as much.

'For such a person, finding a protector might not be so difficult, even in Edinburgh.'

Jean smiled. He might have known that even someone as sensible as Miss van Wiliamsburgh would try to make a play of this sort. It was hard for most people to understand the quality of Céline's love.

'Surely,' said Miss Williamsburgh, 'the poor lady has the right to organise her own rescue at her leisure? I detest being rescued myself, unless I have specifically requested it.'

Jean never doubted himself. But, at the moment, it did strike him that he ought to have thought more about Céline's situation. Perhaps it wouldn't be such a bad idea to be slightly more circumspect about looking for her. He studied Miss van Williamsburgh's unpretentious gown and simply done reddish hair. She was a truly republican woman, the type of a new age. Her strength lay in her innocence, he thought. A servant came by with a tray of bottles.

'More wine?' said Jean.

'I'll have whisky,' said Miss van Williamsburgh. 'Go on. What were you saying?'

*

'Lime and lager,' said Catriona.

'One lime and lager,' repeated Sarah.

'I think that's lager and lime,' said Myrtle, and laughed like a mynah bird. Catriona had never seen anyone like her. She wasn't much over five feet tall and had dead white skin, pipestem arms and a broad grin like a cartoon character. 'And then they painted the walls of his office with a chemical that made him lose his mind,' she was saying to her brother Phil, who was sitting next to her. Catriona gathered that Myrtle was a soap opera fan.

'You could meet anyone in this bar,' said the young man on Catriona's other side. She hadn't caught his name. It sounded like Forgue. The bar was very noisy. 'I've met so many people in our local,' said Forgue. 'I can imagine that,' said Catriona, and she saw the local, dark and quiet and fairly empty, and Forgue in his donkey jacket and tartan scarf listening to an old man talk about mining in Calgary.

Sarah squeezed in beside her. 'This's all right, I would say.' She handed Catriona her glass. 'How did you meet so many people?' asked Catriona. 'My mother met Myrtle at the jazz club,' said Sarah. 'Myrtle plays sax.' 'I don't know much about jazz,' said Catriona. 'I don't know anything,' said Sarah. 'You'll have to come along sometime.'

*

'But would you hope to marry her?' asked Miss van Williamsburgh.

'We could never be respectable in the eyes of the world,' said Jean, 'but that hardly matters.'

'A lady of her background . . . so closely involved with the old régimes —'

'I believe in the perfectability of man,' said Jean with great feeling.

'Forgive me, Citizen Vaubrun. I claim the privilege of age. Perfection is not for the making, or for the keeping, only for the finding. And it is only found in the most unlikely places. One needs to take it while it's there.'

She placed her honest, angular hand on the table, palm up. Jean was unable to resist the impulse to return her smile.

*

The pubs were shut. The chippies were filling up. In the daytime it was mostly older people you saw on the streets of Edinburgh, but late at night everyone was young. They wore black, with make-up, spiky hair, and eerie cheap jewellery. And here was Catriona in the crowd, watching the last of the twilight in York Place.

'You look pretty sober for someone who's just started on whisky,' said Sarah as they walked towards the bus stop.

'I think I'm old enough to be young now,' said Catriona.

'Good, What are you doing?'

'Your friends are really nice. You know?'

'Yeah. Really hospitable. You going anywhere just now?'

'All the way home.'

'Why don't you come back with me?'

'Oh. Well. But this is the last bus.'

'I've got lots of space. And I'll need somebody to wake me up for work tomorrow.'

'You're not that drunk.'

'Not now. But there's more booze at home.'

Catriona laughed. Most people didn't try wit or persuasion on her, drunk or sober. What would Anne think of this? Not very much, one way or the other. Where was it all leading? Too many questions, too many questions, I'm not going to ask any more questions.

'What if we *both* get too drunk to get up for work tomorrow?' she asked as they climbed aboard the bus and put their money in the ticket machine.

'Then my mom will make us coffee,' said Sarah.

*

'She wasn't the woman I came to seek,' said Catriona aloud. She was walking up the Mound to do the lunch shift at the Right and Wrong. It was another close, hazy day, warm enough to wear her Georgian waitress uniform without even a sweater and carry her raincoat under her arm.

She couldn't remember where the verse came from. 'She wasn't the woman I came to seek.' And something about how she did not speak the French of France because she was from Martinique, and how she wasn't rich and she wasn't chic. The verse wasn't about Sarah, of course (she wasn't even from Martinique), but it was just right for her somehow. It was adventurous and yet a bit modest and down-to-earth. Catriona was picturing a series of film-preview shots of Sarah wearing a velvet dress and cape, looking cool and alert but everyday.

She supposed the story would be more *realistic* with someone like Sarah in it, who wasn't glamorous or the love of Jean's life. More mature. Then she thought, hard and suddenly as if it were someone else's thought, I'm in love with someone who's not Anne.

So? she answered herself. It's just a story. Nothing's going to happen.

I don't want to think about it, she went on. It's a nice day. I'm not even dreading work.

Still, she said as she turned the corner of the High Street. I suppose it won't do to let things drift.

Who's letting things drift? she argued. There *isn't* anything to drift.

But it's not, well, responsible to think about it that way.

She was late to the Right and Wrong. Rose-Marie glided up in her clinging black lunch frock, raised her finger and said, as she'd already said several times that day, 'Catreeona, this is your last warning.'

*

Dear Anne,

I'm sorry I didn't write to you before. It's not easy for me to do. I don't know how much you want to hear about anything in particular. But I've thought about it and what's most important to me is being your friend. If that makes a difference to you, I hope you'll write to me.

Catriona wrote her new address and the Right and Wrong's phone number at the bottom. She stood the envelope up on the mantel. I really will post it tomorrow, she thought.

*

It was another lunchtime at the Right and Wrong. There were two separate rushes and someone tried to walk out without paying one of Sarah's tickets. A huge party from the City Chambers arrived without reservations and they had to shove three tables together, and right after that, in came fourteen Japanese tourists.

At two-thirty, Patrice, Sarah, Catriona and the boys were just starting to tackle the clearing-up. They were all tired, though a little richer. Catriona wiped down the last of her tables and suddenly realised that the conversation around her had stopped.

'I think there's somebody here to see you, Catriona,' said one of the boys.

She stood in the doorway with her hand on her hip as she

always did when she was angry. Her dark hair stood up in gelled planes, in the fashion of the time. She was dressed in brilliant white, in a jacket with padded shoulders, Palm Beach trousers, and thick-soled shoes. A shawl from Oxfam in Morningside covered her neck and shoulders.

'Catriona Gough,' she said, her eyes blazing, 'why the fuck didn't you ever write?'

The Third Airedale

Fred Urquhart

My Uncle Geordie, who lived at Dalkeith, had an airedale called Skipper. My Uncle Bill, who lived at Pilton, had an airedale called Captain. When I was a bairn I loathed and feared these dogs, and as my parents often liked to get rid of me I used to stay for short holidays with both uncles, and so I saw more of the dogs than I liked.

I was fond of Uncle Geordie, my mother's youngest brother, but I didn't care for his wife. Auntie Julie was a bossy wee body with a pug nose and a big bust, and she had Uncle Geordie completely under her thumb. She didn't like me either. But I absolutely adored my Uncle Bill, my father's only brother. Uncle Bill was a bachelor, and I liked biding with him best.

There was always Captain and Skipper to contend with, though. I didn't know it then, but I know it now: both dogs were jealous of me. They were used to being the pet of the house, and so whenever I went to my uncles, both dogs never seemed to take their eyes off me and their big mouths were always gaping wide, showing long sharp teeth, and I knew fine they'd like to sink them into me. Uncle Geordie used to laugh and tell me not to be a fearedy-gowk when I said Skipper was trying to bite me. And Auntie Julie was downright sarcastic, always saying: 'Och, you're a spoilt wee brat, Frankie. You think there's nobody in the world but yourself. Skipper likes to be taken notice of, too, ye ken, and I don't see why he shouldn't be. After all, this is his home, and you're just a visitor. He has every right to bare his teeth at ye if he wants to.'

But Uncle Bill always took me on his knee and cuddled me when I said I was afraid of Captain. And he'd tell me stories or sing to me, and sometimes, after he'd had a good tumblerful of whisky, he'd slide his hand up my shorts and stroke my thigh. And sometimes his hand would creep a bit higher, and then when I was near fit to burst with joy he'd stop his tickling and say: 'Ay, but I shouldn't do that, should I? Ye're my young brother's bairn and as innocent as the lamb of God.'

My father was a driver on the electric trams. We lived in a flat at Canonmills overlooking the Water of Leith. My mother took in dressmaking, and she was always busy sewing frocks and blouses for ladies in Inverleith Place and Heriot Row and such like big houses of the neighbourhood. I was an only child, so I daresay I got among her feet a lot before I went to school. We were on the top flat, so I couldn't get out to play; my Ma was feared I'd fall down the stone stairs and break my neck. So as often as could be managed I went for trips with my father on the trams. I sat on the shelf beside the steering-wheel, the shelf that was supposed to be for passengers' parcels and luggage. Often enough it was empty, so I was no trouble to my Dad. I sat there and watched him, and I watched the traffic and the shops on the streets we went through. I had a very good knowledge of Edinburgh by the time I was five. Sometimes Dad was on the Number 23 route, which ran from Bruntsfield to Goldenacre, passing our home. Sometimes he was on the Numbers 8 and

9 routes, which went all the way down to Granton Square. I loved it when we went to Granton, for I was always hoping I'd see Uncle Bill.

Uncle Bill was a joiner in the sawmill at Granton. He lived a couple of miles away in a cottage on a farm at Pilton, a cottage where he and my Dad were born. My grandfather had been the grieve on the farm. When grandfather died the farmer had allowed my grandmother and her two sons, still in their teens, to stay on in the cottage because he didn't need a new grieve; he had an unmarried son in the big farmhouse, ready to take on the job. Uncle Bill had looked after my grandmother until she died when I was a baby. He was twenty-five then and didn't want to get married, so he kept on the cottage and looked after himself. He cycled to Granton and back every day.

At the weekends when my Ma and Dad wanted a bit of peace, it was usually easier to send me to bide with Uncle Bill than to take me in the bus to my Uncle Geordie at Dalkeith. But they always gave me the choice first and put me in a dilemma, though I didn't know the meaning of the word then. On one hand, Uncle Geordie and Auntie Julie took me to the pictures on Saturday nights to see Tom Mix and Buck Jones. I was just old enough to become crazy about cowboy films, but even handsome Buck Jones couldn't make me like Auntie Julie any better. So I mostly chose Uncle Bill because I thought the world of him, but I was cunning enough to go to Uncle Geordie's about every fourth week.

Early on Saturday morning Dad would take me in a tram down to Granton Square, and there Uncle Bill would be waiting. I was always so glad to see him I hardly ever took time to say goodbye to Dad and whichever conductor was on tram-duty with him. Uncle Bill would perch me on the handlebars of his bicycle and we'd spin along Lower Granton Road beside the railway lines, with engines and strings of wagons shunting close to us and the engine-drivers shouting hello to Uncle Bill, and beyond them were the masts and funnels of ships in the harbour. Then when we got to the sawmill I'd stay close beside Uncle Bill watching him sawing and planing, keeping well away from the saw, until midday when the mill shut up for the week. And then we'd cycle to Pilton, and I was completely happy beside my big fine-looking uncle with his shiny blue-black hair while he made some dinner, and then we'd potter about all afternoon in his garden and his little greenhouse. It was the happiest time of my life. The only snag was that big smelly dog Captain that kept nosing in between me and Uncle Bill, always glaring at me and showing his big white teeth.

I thought of this and other things that happened over seventy years ago after I went to the supermarket last Friday to do my week's shopping. I was in the fruit and vegetable section waiting to weigh some potatoes on the scales when I saw a bairn of about three years old, a bonnie wee lad with fair hair and big dark blue eyes, picking apples out of the bin and shoving them into his mother's shopping bag. She was so busy talking to another woman, who was weighing onions, that she never noticed what the wee fellow was doing. So I took it upon myself to tell her, old nosey-parker that I am. I knew she'd better be told, otherwise she'd get a bonnie fright when she was stopped at the paydesk and accused of shoplifting. She got a big enough fright when I said: 'Excuse me, but your wee laddie is filling your bag with apples that I'm sure you'll not be wanting. I daresay he wants them — don't you, sonny? — but I don't think your mammy 'll want them.'

The poor young woman, a pretty creature, flushed scarlet and said: 'Oh, Junior, you naughty little boy! If you do that again I'll smack your bottom.'

The little shrimp giggled, then he looked up at her and then at me and said: 'I don't care if you smack my bottom, Mummy. That's what you said to Daddy last week when he said he'd do it to you. I was playing with my trucks and my action garage, and I heard you say you liked it.'

'Really, kids!' the young woman cried. 'My God, they do give you a red face when you're least expecting it.'

I laughed and said I was the same when I was young. My Ma often didn't know where to look when I came out with things about Uncle Geordie and Auntie Julie. I was moving forward to weigh my potatoes when the little boy caught hold of my coat. 'I like this nice man,' he said. 'Will he get me some apples?'

'Junior!' his mother cried. 'What a sauce you've got!'

I chatted with her while I weighed the potatoes, then I moved off to the wines and spirits section. The little boy pattered along beside me, looking up and smiling. He took my free hand and said: 'I'm going with you, man.'

He gave a roar of rage when his mother pulled him back, saying: 'Now behave yourself, Junior, or this is the last time I'll bring you into the supermarket. I'll leave you in the car with Caesar after this.'

I shook my head and shrugged my shoulders at her, trying not to look into the child's large eyes filling with tears as he gazed petulantly at me, his underlip thrust out. I waved goodbye and went round the corner to the wines and spirits. I could not help but remember myself, another pretty fair-haired boy, who also wanted his own way at that age, and how I wound Uncle Bill's heart round my little finger and was perhaps responsible for the tragedy caused by a savagely jealous dog.

My mind went back to one particular Saturday evening. It was after tea, getting dark, and Uncle Bill couldn't do anything in his garden. He sat down in the big easy-chair beside the kitchen range, took me on his knee and read me a story. I had one arm around his neck and was leaning my head against his chest. When he finished reading, he began to sing his favourite song, *If You Were The Only Girl In The World And I Was The Only Boy*, except he turned the words round — for a laugh, he always said — and sang: 'If I was the only girl in the world and you were the only boy . . .' And then suddenly he said: 'What's that on your leg, son? It's not blood, is it? Och no, it's just jam you've dropped. You're a right clairty wee boy, aren't you! We'll have to get it off before you go to bed.'

And he bent down and licked off the jam. Then he pretended he was Captain going to bite me. He growled and touched my thigh with his teeth. 'What lovely wee pink hams you've got, son. How would you like it if I was the wolf in Red Riding Hood?' He pressed his lips and the faint touch of his teeth farther up my thigh. Then he slid his left hand down the back of my little short trousers, splaying his fingers across my bare bottom, and started to tickle me. I was squealing with delight at the tricks his middle finger was playing when suddenly Captain leapt on us growling. The dog reared on his hind paws, his wide open mouth almost gripping my face, his front paws scrabbling and scratching at both of us. I screamed at the nearness of his shark-like pointed white teeth. Uncle Bill let out a yell and kicked him away, then he snapped on Captain's lead and tied him to a chair in the corner of the kitchen. I heard Uncle Bill mutter:

'Maybe you're right, dog, I'd gone far enough.' Or I thought I heard these words, for Captain was growling so fiercely, I wasn't sure.

I was still weeping with fright when Uncle Bill put me to bed. His kisses and cuddles soothed me, and I stopped crying when he said: 'He's a bad dog, and I'll give him a good hiding for that.'

Uncle Bill's best pal was Bernard Leslie, who worked in a barber's shop at Goldenacre. My Ma used to take me there, and Bernard would cut my hair for fourpence. 'Will I give ye a jail crop, son?' he usually said, and he would grin and wink at my Ma. 'I don't think our wee gentleman would like that, Peggy!'

'And neither would I,' my Ma always said. 'So less of your havers, Bernard, and get on with the job. I haven't got all day if you have.'

Often at weekends Bernard would come to Pilton and stay the night with Uncle Bill and me. After supper Uncle Bill would put me, as he always did, in the big double bed in the room next the kitchen, and then he'd leave the door open, and I'd lie and listen to him and Bernard yarning, wondering how soon it would be before they got into bed, one on either side of me. Though I was usually asleep before that happened. And now I wonder if it ever really happened. For on some mornings I'd wake up lying, well wrapped in blankets, on the sofa. Sometimes I'd wake up and find I was the only one in the middle of the big bed. It was only sometimes that I'd wake and find Bernard snoring on one side of me and Uncle Bill giving an occasional snort on the other. Always they were naked, and I was surprised they didn't wear pyjamas or a nightshirt like me. Not that I cared. I snuggled up against their nakedness and was content.

I was in bed but not asleep one night when my father came home. I waited for him to come into my room and say hello. Instead I heard him talking excitedly to my Ma. I couldn't hear the first words, then I heard: 'Bill phoned the depot and told me about the accident.'

'What accident?' Ma said.

'I'm tellin' you, woman. The accident to poor Bernard. D'you never listen! He got his arse all torn away by that bloody dog.'

'The arse of his breeks?' Ma said. 'Poor Bernard, I must see if I can sew it for him. Though I daresay it'll be a difficult job.'

'Not his breeks, woman,' Dad said. 'More's the pity it wasn't just that. I always maintained Captain was vicious. It's his bare arse that's been mauled.'

'His bare arse?' Ma said. 'What was he doing naked?'

'I dunno,' Dad said. 'I daresay he and Bill were larking about and the dog thought he'd join in.'

'Funny way to go on,' Ma said. 'Poor Bernard.'

'Poor Bill you mean. He could be liable for damages if it comes to court. Bernard's in the infirmary and is having to lie on his belly.'

Captain was taken to the vet's and destroyed. When Bernard came out of hospital he did not walk very well for a good long time. He sold his bicycle and stopped being Uncle Bill's best pal. He married a nurse not long after that. I never saw her, and I don't remember ever seeing Bernard again either. Ma took me to another barber's in Stockbridge.

After I started school I didn't go so often to Uncle Bill's. It didn't seem quite the same, anyway, as I got bigger. He didn't take me on his knee any longer, and I slept in a bed of my own. He never got another dog to replace Captain. I was pleased about that because I still had to contend with Skipper when I went to Uncle Geordie's. Even the compensation of going to the Saturday matinee on my own to see Buck Jones or Hoot Gibson and then again at night with Uncle Geordie and his wife to another picture house for the big film of the week — Clara Bow or Norma Talmadge or some star like that — didn't make up for the way Skipper kept eyeing me and slavering.

When I was about twelve the farm at Pilton was sold, and Uncle Bill had to leave his cottage. At the same time the Granton sawmill stopped working. Uncle Bill got a job in a joiner's shop out Haymarket way and he moved to lodgings in Dalry Road. I never went there to stay, but I was always glad when he visited us at Canonmills. He had one or two best pals after Bernard, but I never took to any of them; and as he got older he never brought anybody with him when he came on a visit. I went oftener to Uncle Geordie's by that time and sometimes I missed Uncle Bill if he came to see Dad and Ma on a Saturday night. Uncle Bill died of pneumonia in his middle forties. I still remember him, after all those years, as one of the best-looking men I ever saw I've never loved anyone in the same way since.

I ran into the little fair-haired boy and his mother again in the queue at the paydesk. Or I should say the wee imp ran into me. I was doing some mental arithmetic, counting up what was in my wire basket, when I got a great dig in the backside. It was the wee lad shoving his basket into me and laughing fit to burst when I turned and looked down at him.

'Junior!' his mother cried. 'Say you're sorry to the gentleman for bumping into him.'

'He likes it,' the shrimp said, giving my bum another dig. 'Don't you, nice man?'

'Stop it at once, Junior,' she said.

'It's all right,' I said. 'I don't mind if he's getting some fun out of it. But maybe it would be better, son, if you put your basket on the counter, and then we can watch it slide along to the cash-register.'

I put the basket on the counter and held onto it to keep it from banging into the shopping of the woman in front. The wee lad put his hand on my haunch, then he slid it round and took a firm grip of my trousers. While I put my purchases on the sliding counter he kept patting the inside of my thigh until it drove me to desperation. I kept talking to his mother and the girl at the cash-register, but I was so distracted that I didn't know what I was saying. At last I found myself offering to help her and Junior and their trolley-load to the car park.

We had no sooner got out of the supermarket's doors than the wee imp said he was tired and I must carry him to the car. His mother protested, and he started to cry. So, much against my better judgement, I put my own shopping bag on top of his mother's trolley and picked him up. He put his arms around my neck, almost strangling me, and snuggled his cheek against mine. 'I like you, nice man,' he said. 'Will you be my new granddaddy?'

As we walked along the path to the supermarket's car park, I realised the danger susceptible adults like me were in from precocious and promiscuous children like this. Although the lad was not, I judged, more than three years old, he was well aware already of his charisma and his potential, and he'd become more conscious of it as he grew older and would have no qualms about dragging the adults he fancied into his net. I began to sweat, and it was not because of the boy's weight.

'I think I've carried you far enough, sonny,' I said. 'I'll put you down now.'

I realised I'd made a mistake as soon as he tightened his arms around my neck. I should have put him down before I said anything. 'I don't want to walk,' he wailed. 'I'm tired, tired, tired. Junior wants granddaddy to carry him right to the car.'

I had to comply, and so, to lessen my growing awareness of danger, I tried to slacken the contact my arms were making with his smooth chubby hurdies. He kept rubbing his cheek against mine, and so I was thankful when his mother stopped her trolley at the back of a bright red Mercedes.

A big young man uncurled himself from the driving seat, stretched to his full six feet two, and yawned. I was dumbfounded at the sight of his shiny blue-black hair, his long-lashed blue eyes and his brown face. He was so like Uncle Bill that my heart turned over. Uncle Bill as he was at the age of twenty-eight over seventy years ago. Except that Uncle Bill had never worn skin-tight pale blue jeans and an expensive thick multi-coloured polo sweater. Nor had Uncle Bill a loud officious English voice like this young man.

He said: 'Thought you were never coming, dear. Have you been buying the whole store?'

'No, darling, just the usual,' she said. 'Sorry we're a bit late, but Junior got tired, and this nice gentleman offered to carry him here.'

'Why couldn't he have sat on the trolley like he always

does?' her husband said. Then to me: 'Thank you very much for your assistance, sir. It was very civil of you.'

I don't like being called sir, and the way he said it made my flesh grue. It was the way a policeman talks when he has his notebook out and is asking questions. Maybe this big black-haired man was a policeman? Or a detective off duty? I didn't like him, resemblance or no resemblance to Uncle Bill.

And here was Captain jumping out of the back of the car, showing his shark's teeth in a welcoming snarl. It was the first airedale I'd seen for years, maybe the first since the two that shadowed my childhood. and airedales were no different now from what they were then. This one leapt on me at the exact moment that Junior unloosened his arms and thrust himself into his father's crying: 'Daddy, Daddy, I like this nice man. He's my new granddaddy, but I like my Daddy best.'

The airedale grasped my right arm in his mouth. I couldn't prevent a yell of fright. 'Down, Caesar, down,' the young man ordered. 'Leave. At once, sir!'

The dog released his grip. The young woman cried: 'Has he hurt you? Has he torn your sleeve?'

While I examined my sleeve, which had only a slight tear, the dog leapt up on the young man and the child, his open mouth only inches from the little boy's legs.

'Down. Caesar, down when I tell you,' the young man shouted.

'Down, Caesar, the child cried. 'Bad dog! Smack his bottom, Daddy.'

'I'll do just that,' the man said. 'Hand me that leash from the back seat, Betty.'

The young woman handed the leash to her husband. He raised it threateningly above the airedale which was now crouching slavishly at his feet. He bent down, snapped the leash on the dog's collar, then pulled the dog up on a very tight lead. 'We'll give you some exercise to take the juice out of you, dog,' he said. 'Come on, Betty, lock the car. We'll walk up to Clark's and Joseph's to get new batteries for the radio and a few other odds and ends. Thank you very much for your assistance, sir. You're sure you're all right? Goodbye.'

And he walked away with Junior on his shoulder and the dog being almost throttled by the tightened lead. 'Bye-bye, nice man,' Junior called. And his mother gave me an apologetic smile and said something I didn't catch as she hurried after husband and son.

I watched until they went out of the car park, then I walked slowly to my own car. I was wondering how long it would be before Caesar followed Captain's example and took a bite out of Junior. I'm still wondering. I'm sure that one of those days the dog's jealousy and the child's charisma, or the combination of both, will lead to grief.

Crush Me Tender, Love Me Blue

Toni Davidson

THE MAN'S sharp instincts surface and he sees an unusual figure. He sharpens the focus to the right leg and quickens his walk immediately. He plots a path to veer and to avoid, to watch cars flashing by smiling at blank, unknown faces in mutual avoidance. And then he's made it, horror shy, homeward bound.

Andrew walks away from the receding back, carrying the newspaper and milk with hands that tighten with every step to show white knuckles erupt on red skin.

Muddled sixties jargon, lurid colours and ricocheting bullets fly past him, missing him by inches as he enters the flat and yet he is unaware of either the television or his lover in bed. He passes into the kitchen without a word.

Iain looked up when Andrew came in but quickly returned his attention to the screen when he heard the volley of shots and his lips parted slightly at the crescendo of violence and glamour. It ends and his neck muscles relax, relieved of tension, and he pulls the ashtray onto his bare chest, holding the cigarette contemplatively in his mouth. His mood has been set by what he has witnessed. Morning thoughts turn the afternoon predictable.

Andrew appears at the door. He throws Iain the paper.

'Coffee?'

'Coffee yeah.'

'Toast?'

'Yeah, toast.'

'Talkative?'

'No, never talkative.'

Andrew fills the kettle, metal on metal as the spout grates against the tap. He leans back against the wall, seeing his face in the cracked, diamond-shaped mirror and he sifts through his thoughts, trying to hold back the vitriol while searching his face for yet more mutations. But mutations of what? A perfect form? He smiles but then doesn't.

He feels searing anger, not constructive, not realistic, not tolerant; no way clear to seeing the other point of view. Just anger. The same anger he feels towards the morning greetings from his colleagues at the library. Simpering their patronage to fuel their self-righteousness. But he smiles back — of course — because he can't do anything else for he is ill at ease, they are ill at ease and they all drown in smiles that suffocate.

Then comes the whip, the sudden vicious reminder of the man in the street. His oh-so-careful slimy grin that lashed out and maimed as much as a punch or a kick. His neat, Astaire-like side-step to the road where he would rather die under a shining new Merc than to have to go too close to a cripple. But the roles are assigned and Andrew knows his role so well now. He is not to retaliate and must always be happy; thankful for all the help he has received and act like a fucking Samaritan to those worse off then himself. To walk and think and live like a puppet.

He smiles at the reflection in the mirror and it too adopts the smile that says nothing. No betrayal of inner thoughts. He turns to the kettle and makes the coffee. He takes the mugs to the side of the bed and sits by the feet of his lover.

Iain is staring but not seeing. His eyes fixed and dilated. He feels the effects of the night before, of a beat struck many times last night and last year. His ears still have that ringing that seems to have become part of his headache. The taste in his mouth is stale and he blows his breath onto the palm of his hand to discover it is foul. And he notices his lover's leg for the first time since the last time. Why now? Why then?

They walk out together holding hands (but only in their minds). They walk slowly, Iain checking his pace to Andrew's naturally awkward step. He gave up being permanently conscious of Andrew's disability soon after they first met yet he hangs on, thinking that Andrew himself quite obviously can't forget.

It seems to him that he is only really preoccupied with Andrew's leg when he thinks that Andrew is himself.

His brow furrows, the grooves of skin that ridge his forehead a natural thing he was born with. He dwells on the dilemma that he inherited along with his love for this man that he questions as sympathy.

Andrew is aware of Iain's thoughts — he recognises the mood. A mood which seems to be slipped into more and more frequently as the months have elapsed since they first met. But he doesn't review them, he doesn't try to straighten out the sheets yet again — not now anyway. He finds that he has to have his full concentration on his walk in order to match Iain's stumbling, neurotic empathy.

He smiles to himself, reflecting how the roles of the Samaritan have gone back and forth in their relationship.

And as they walk staccato, carefully avoiding any bumps or pitfalls that will affect their stride, each gets lost in a world that is so familiar to them now. Memories as epileptic twinges that fade out reality, that causes their minds to go reluctantly back to another time, another place where they hardly ever go now except in their dreams and in their nightmares. And there are fleeting recollections which occur much more frequently and these short bursts of remembrance act and feel like the brisk slash of a knife.

In Iain's world he remembers the meeting in a bar. The sense of immediate attraction to this skinny guy with the bad acne and the eyebrows that met. The conversation that was always meant to lead somewhere and then Iain's surprise when he watched Andrew walk to the toilet. He smiled for a moment thinking it was a joke (a slash of the knife at this point) and then the smile turned to disbelief — 'he didn't look disabled' — finally he felt embarrassment that he had progressed through such sensational thoughts. When Andrew returned he found himself almost asking the question, 'so how long have you been disabled?'. And yet they eventually did talk about 'the leg' and then 'the disease' and Iain heard the word 'Spinabifida'; a word previously heard only on

TV when charities were appealing for money. That night it didn't matter; maybe he was just feeling horny and although this guy was disabled he was still cute (another slash of the knife for that one). But he got 'caught', this one couldn't be brushed off so easily and now, ten months later, he was in a situation that he both loves and hates.

He fell in love with the man, the political doubts about sexuality and disability came later as he learnt more and his mind slowly opened and then contracted with knowledge that proved to be no salvation. He found he could no longer hide behind a naive love, a sensuous world of uncomplex bohemia and he was drawn, still yearning for past ignorance, not up or down, but along to a state of affairs that simply put he could not cope with. The easy life he had known seemed to have suddenly stopped.

In Andrew's world the pocket-knife that belonged to Iain's recollection became a cleaver that seemed to go so close to the bone as to almost sever completely. And if he puts his hand to his forehead he can feel the scars of ridged skin that *he* wasn't born with and it is as if each rippled furrow represents, records each recollective twinge.

With a slash of knife, the hospital, the prison — he had many names for the school where he was both patient and prisoner but never a pupil — comes slithering into his mind. With a slash of the knife he remembers when he was twelve, lying face down on the landing, watching and listening to his parents arguing about him and his future. These arguments, which often became violent, implanted in the parents an entrenched bitterness that surfaced as hate to Andrew's face. So vehement sometimes was this resentment that he could do nothing but believe it. The estrangement became even more profound when he told them that he was gay. His role of mutant son extended itself to incorporate pervert as well. Thus labelled, it relinquished the parents of their last shred of moral obligation to their son; even managed to convince them that in the end none of it was their fault. He was a bad lot and it was just one of those things.

And now he was here, a different life, learning not to forget his past and not trying to hide or run away from it but rather learning how to hit back, to use the overwhelming anger he had in him to both constructive and destructive ends.

They both continue walking, heading for cafés and silent cappucinos drunk with modest, defensive smiles.

In the park, after a long, sporadically talkative meal, they walk with a more even step, the long avenue of silver birch trees ahead of them straightening their path after the awkward descent from the main road. They have walked through this park in different states of mind and various styles of walking and staggering with Iain sometimes crying for no reason and Andrew's face set resolute on the path ahead of him. Or sometimes Andrew had been so drunk that Iain shouldered him all the way home. There had been sex too; stumbling, frenetic rush to behind the sculptured bushes — carved in images of birds caught in flight — and the pulling of clothes, the trembling with fright and lust and the quiet, the absolute deathness of the park at night. They lay there covered in soil and broken branches, their breath aching in repressed pants, the post-climax moment unhurried by blind fumbling for a towel. The walk back from that moment had been silent but the closeness between them shocked and frightened them both.

Still in their independent reveries they walk closely together as they near the end of the park. Iain feels the effects of the alcohol drunk with the meal but it has made him feel good, giving him a sense — true or not — that he can cope, that he can deal with the way his own mind and from there be able to deal with other people's. For Andrew alcohol gives no such release for mental biopsy, his examinations always seem to take place in a sober frame of mind and quite often match the skill of doctor's probe. If anything has been achieved in this closeness it is a vow to retrace his steps, to remember and confront the house full of ghosts that have become his past. He smiles slightly at the vague feeling of hope he now feels. Both of them jump back slightly as a cat darts in front of them as they leave the park, they both watch it running across the road without looking and then scramble up a wall to window ledge. As they pass it remains there, still and unwavering in its gaze into the lighted room.

Andrew undresses him slowly, taking each bit of clothing off slowly but then flinging them into a corner of the room ('so you won't find them in the morning'). He pulls down the boxer shorts last and kisses the erection lying twitching on Iain's stomach.

Iain pushes him off and lays him flat on the bed. He pins

Andrew's arms against the mattress while their lips twist together, Iain increasing the pressure on Andrew's right leg so that he can't move. He lets go suddenly and takes off Andrew's shirt, throwing it quickly into the corner where his own shirt was thrown. He pulls down the jeans, being careful not to pull the bag off, and he discards these as well. The head of Andrew's cock strains in its clinical, plastic vice — there out of necessity and there where Iain's hands have so often passed over. Tonight he holds back the ill-concealed shudders and caresses the swelling head, he bends and kisses the skin exposed. Andrew pushes him off and then pins him down. Raising his head from Iain's he stares at him, his hair lightly brushing his eyes. They stay still, eyes locked together and Iain smiles but Andrew says nothing with his mouth but keeps pouring his love out of his eyes into Iain's. Exhausted, Andrew lowers his head and their tongues meet and Andrew slides down and hugs Iain's legs, hoping that they will become immobile and lock him in this position and never separate.

Friday: Two Richards

George McAlpine

The street below was quiet as ever. At half-past five he leant closer to the window and strained to see into the flat opposite. His breath misted the cold glass and he turned away, indifferent to others' arguments. He crouched before the bookcase and ran his eyes along the tightly packed, fading broken spines of familiar paperbacks, reading names and titles.

He returned to his coffee and drank, switched on the TV and flicked through soundless channels of familiar images, crouching to watch the dull face of a man in a suit. The video sat on the floor and a tape was in the machine. He switched to the video channel and turned the machine on.

He lay back on the couch and watched the camera pan a sundrenched American cityscape and dip between the buildings into a traffic-clogged street.

He lit another cigarette. The camera settled across the street from a windowless exterior set in a row of shopfronts. Above the door a simply painted sign read *Eagle*. Seen through the passing traffic a bearded man in an army cap and mirror shades emerged — the bulging muscles of his torso scantily covered by a black vest — jacket thrown casually over the shoulder — he paused and then walked slowly off the screen.

The door swung open again and a blond man as muscled

as the first and cleanshaven in white T-shirt and faded jeans paused casually at the kerb, looked right then left and walked after the bearded man.

A quiet street and the beard stood in the shade of an apartment block doorway. The noise of the traffic gave way to the beginnings of a disco beat. The blond man's T-shirt had been removed and tucked into his belt so it hung limply behind him. He stopped before the beard and they entered the building together.

The screen filled with a hard cock swinging loose from tight faded jeans. The beard parted and a dark red mouth edged with pure white American teeth engulfed the cock. The camera retreated and the dark head began bobbing back and forth swallowing and regurgitating and a hand cupped the blond balls. Another hand snaked up the chest and pinched tight on a nipple. The blond head bent over watching and obscuring the face.

He watched, attention fixed on the screen, as the men stripped each other and the blond pushed the bearded man face down on the floor, bound the exposed balls with a thin strip of leather and pulled. The buttocks jumped upwards to be slapped red. Then pushed his impossibly large dick into the hole and fucked.

He watched the scenes and the men change and slow motion cum fly through the air. He opened his fly and grabbed his balls and pulled in imitation. A succession of genitals were bound and tits clamped and stretched against the music's insistent rhythm. The orgasm was slow and exhausting, blending subtly with the pain of twisted balls and soaking the front of his shirt.

*

He felt his face still flushed from the heat of the shower. Behind him on the back seats of the bus four teenagers argued loudly over the cost of the litre of cider and half bottle of vodka they passed between them.

A head with close-cropped hair appeared at the top of the stairs and seeing Martin, smiled.

'Hi Paul, how're you doing?'

Paul sat beside him.

'Not bad, broke as usual but surviving. Y'off to see Gerry?'

'No, just out for a pint or two. There's nothing on telly. I'm meeting him later at the disco after his work.'

Paul laughed. 'It's not even seven o'clock, you won't be able to stand by then.'

'You never know, I might get lucky. This is my stop.'

'Best of luck anyway, see you later.'

'See you.' He made his way unsteadily downstairs as the bus turned into Argyle Street.

*

As he approached details became clear: the anxious face of a young man framed by the jacket's collar pulled tight around the neck, shoulders hunched. A blue light sweeping across the almost empty bar caught the young face occasionally in strange shadows. Martin stopped a few feet before him and stood with legs planted firmly apart, said loud enough to be heard above the music, 'What are you drinking?'

The face jerked into an uneasy smile and said, 'Lager.'

Richard stepped into the flat silently and saw only that they were in a wide hallway before the door closed behind him. The lock clicked noisily into place. He stood in the darkness and heard the other man move to the left and a door open and saw the rectangle of lighter grey.

The room was large and square with high ceiling and two tall curtainless windows. A black leather suite was arranged around a white marble fireplace standing starkly against slate-grey walls and carpet. Plants around the room eased the harshness of the simple colours and lines.

Richard took the offered mug of coffee and sat. Martin slouched on the couch beside him and began unlacing his boots. He watched as Richard's head dipped and his full lips opened to sip coffee. The skin around Richard's eyes was pulled tight with tension.

Richard looked up and his lips relaxed into a slight smile. His eyes flicked away again and he stood suddenly. He took cigarettes from his jacket, offered Martin one and lit it.

He took smoke into his lungs and exhaled slowly. He smiled contentedly and lay back on the couch. Martin's arm slipped around him.

*

The arm uncurled onto Richard's chest and moved there over the nipples and down onto the tensing stomach.

Martin held the nipple in his teeth and squeezed hard stubble rasping the skin above, squeezed harder and the pain began. Suddenly abandoned by the mouth the nipple hot with bites cold with saliva in the cooling air. The other bitten and feeling contracted to twin points, sharp and stinging as the teeth cut in. Richard laughed at a vision of the nipple cut off and stuck like a baby's dummy in Martin's mouth.

Martin rose and straddled Richard's chest. The cock went in the mouth. His hand moved to his chest and felt the nipples intact but saliva like blood drying quickly, only the throbbing tenderness remained. Richard gagged as it pushed too far head trapped against the pillow but it pulled back out. He licked it, the tip, little mouth oozing moisture, feeling the smoothness on the tongue. Martin groaned closed eyes and moved forward with his hips. Richard moved his tongue on the roundness and the ragged break and the folds of foreskin wrinkled and pulled tight.

The mouth emptied and Martin knelt between the open legs, his hands running up and down the thighs hair under his hands bristling and tickling almost. His cock lay against Richard's and his hand searched underneath for a hole gently probing. He ripped a packet in his hand and smoothed the rubber on his cock making it shine in the half light as Richard raised his head and watched. He lifted the legs. The cock moved between arsehole and scrotum. So intently watching himself he no longer saw Richard and he pushed a finger smeared with cold gell gently into the hole, then the cock pressed against the opening and pushed. Richard opened slowly and then the cock was in and he could see only Martin's glistening blond hair between his legs.

Martin pushed and in the centre of Richard's belly was pain. He stopped and then small movements back and forward and the warmth began like a tongue inside his lapping. He remembered suddenly to breath, was pushed into, moving with the breathing. His legs rose and ankles rested on shoulders. Martin held him at the knees always pushing inside him like warm water pouring in.

He pulled out and turned Richard over and lifted his hips and entered him again. He lay covering him, the cock fully in, hair and balls pressed into buttocks. Richard's face pressed into the pillow under the unmoving weight. Cotton pillowcase smelling of sweat filled his nose, eyes, mouth, a sharp searing pain on his shoulder. His stomach contracted and dull pain in his empty lungs spread. The cock jabbed once, twice and Richard came, blackness in his head turning red. He gripped the sheet with both hands and threw back his head gulping air.

*

They stood naked next to each other at the bathroom sink brushing their teeth. Richard used a new toothbrush which Martin had been saving fresh from the cellophane. He watched Richard in the mirror, newly combed hair oddly neat against unshaven chin and eyes dull with tiredness. His arm touched Martin's occasionally as he brushed with short back and forth movements at the front of his mouth and then the toothbrush plunging to the back. With the movement his cock swung, hitting against the side of the sink. Martin spat out the toothpaste and watched the cock as he bent to rinse his mouth in running water. He stood straight and breathed through his mouth tasting mint coolness.

*

Gerry's voice was gentle, quiet and coaxing on the phone, 'Do you remember Andy?'

'The new barman?' Martin watched Richard through the open bedroom doorway, pulling on underpants and jeans.

'Yes, that's the one. Well, he's having a party tonight.'

'And you want to go.' Martin tried hard not to sound annoyed.

'Well he has invited me.'

'And you want into his knickers,' he added a little laugh to put Gerry at ease.

'He's practically offered.'

'Will I see you tomorrow or will you go straight to work?'

'Oh God, thanks Martin!' Gerry's gratitude was excessive. 'I don't have to come in tomorrow, I've persuaded Carol to do my shift. I'll come up tomorrow afternoon and make it up to you.'

'There's nothing to make up, enjoy yourself.' Martin allowed himself to be magnanimous.

'You're an angel, see you tomorrow.'

Through the bedroom doorway Martin saw Richard carefully examining an old battered tawse which earlier had lain unnoticed beside the bed. He looked round uneasily as Martin put down the phone and said that he had to go.

They walked to the end of the road together. Richard turned left for the underground, Martin hailed a taxi.

*

With his third pint in hand Martin leant against the wall in a darkened corner watching men passing to the bar or the toilets. His knees ached gently and his eyes watered with tiredness and the smoke of his own cigarette. His T-shirt clung to the sweat on his back and chest. When he moved he was dizzy with drink. A song which was almost familiar began and a wave of men passed to the dancefloor another wave returning. He mumbled words and phrases from the song quietly enough for the noise to drown them until a man returned to his side and stopped. He picked a half empty glass from the floor and handed it to the man.

'Will we go after this drink . . . I'm sorry. I've forgotten your name.'

'Martin,' Martin said. 'I've forgotten yours.'

'Richard. I've only had a couple, I can drive.'

'Where do you live?'
'Motherwell.'
'We'll go to mine. I'm just off Byres Road.'

*

Richard rested his aching arm and the cock in his hand was almost soft like his own. The hair on his stomach was matted with cum. He was close to sleep and his words slurred when he spoke. 'Did you come?'

'I don't think I'm going to, a bit too much to drink,' Martin whispered hoarsely and coughed. 'Did you?'

'Yes, ages ago.'

Martin took time to reply, 'Sorry I never managed. I came twice tonight already.' They lay in silence for a moment. 'Thanks for keeping going.'

Richard adjusted his position so a gap separated them, 'Don't mention it.'

Martin turned to face Richard and felt his breath on his face. He turned away again.

Richard mumbled, 'Did you set the alarm?'

'Seven o'clock.' Martin snuggled his face into the pillow and sighed.

Richard turned to face the wall. Their buttocks touched slightly and they moved apart. 'I can't be late for work,' Richard said.

Addicted to Suicide

JANE CARNALL

SHE WAS an assassin, a good one, the best of the upper-Level illegits, the unbraceleted.

She was a telepath, too, a mindwalker. She allowed some of those who employed her to know that, by subtle hints and occasional, seemingly involuntary revealings. They trusted her for it; an outlier psion could not go running to Them and reveal who hired her and for what reason. And they despised her for it, some of them, and they feared her for it, most of them; but she did not care, so long as they paid her enough to be drunk on until the need to kill was irresistible again. She was nameless; they called her Fox, for her sandy hair and brows, for the sharply blue eyes that seemed to rake through you and see nothing of interest.

She slept alone in secret places, and not even enough alcohol to send a mudwrestler under the table would slow her assassin's reflexes. She killed smiling, and there were few who, having seen her kill, wanted even to risk dying at her hands.

And there was a boy and a dog. The boy was small, quiet-moving, desperately inoffensive. He was a legit, braceleted, but he never seemed to have any money, and somehow he seemed to avoid the gangs, legit and illegit, that roamed the upper Levels. He had not, as far as anyone knew, not that anyone cared, yet been beaten up or raped. This was probably due to the dog, a black and silver shadow following protectively at the boy's heels. It was not an animal you'd care to tangle with, not even for the sake of the high-k meat that clung to its bones, not while rats were smaller and had less impressive jaws and could, besides, be sold to the lower-Level kind for a bounty of six minims per head, not to mention what their meat and skin would fetch.

Around the edges of the World spiralled the ancient stairs, where rats and sometimes other creatures bred. People slept there, too, sometimes, when they were poor and weary enough to risk the rats and the police-gangs. There was a place under the flight of stairs like a hidden cave, in the shadow of long-fused light-panels, where the assassin slept, among other places. She did not fear the rats; a certain set of mind would keep them away from her in small furry terror, and as for the police-gangs, she could be awake and away before ever they reached her. She curled up in the darkest corner, pillowing her head on her arm, and clung to the memory of four hours before, when the time had stilled and she had been not, sweet tearing bliss. . . .

She was woken by a boy and a dog practically falling over her, and rolled to her feet in an instant, pulling her knife from its hidden sheath, knocking the small skinny body to the floor and kneeling over it, her knife to its throat –

If she had killed less recently, the boy would have died. But a moment's hesitation, and a strange lethargy spread through her, so that she did not struggle when the dog leapt on her, snarling. Apathetic, not hungry to kill and die, not afraid, not angry, not even hating. Only a strange peace and stillness. *Now I die for the last time.*

On her back, with the dog's jaws at her throat, she waited

to not-exist. She heard the boy scramble to his feet, the uncertain, worried voice: 'Wolf – you haven't – she's not dead?'

A quicksilver sending traced the edge of her mind. 'Don't kill her. Please –'

He knelt down beside the dog, staring into her face in the meagre light from the outer stairway. 'Sorry. We didn't know you were in here. If Wolf lets you up, you won't hurt us?'

'You would do better ordering your animal to kill me.'

'I don't – don't –' the boy was almost stammering. 'Wolf, please let her up, I don't think she'll hurt us.'

The dog released her and moved back, a low growl rumbling in its throat. The lassitude still on her, she came slowly to her feet and looked down at the boy, who stood up, shifting uneasily. A glint of light caught something on his wrist. She seized his arm, turning him to see better, knowing it was a citizen bracelet. Only it was green.

'You're a psion,' she said aloud. 'A *legit* psion.'

He shrugged, looking very small and very harmless. Fox didn't believe it for a minute.

'So what's a legit doing sleeping on the stairs? For that matter what's a psion doing away from Level 13?'

'They threw me out,' the boy said softly. 'They said I wasn't any use to Them.'

'No use? Hnh. What are you, a schizo?'

He shook his head. She understood, suddenly, the cause of this weird peace, and shielded, snarling, 'Damn – you're an *empath*!'

The dog growled, showing sharp white teeth, and the boy shivered. 'I'm sorry –' he began, and then started violently. 'I c- I can't *reach* you –'

'You didn't answer the question,' Fox said impatiently. 'If

you're legit, you have to have a room allowance. So why are you trying to sleep out here?'

'I can't feed Wolf and me on the allowance and rent a room.' The boy glanced down at the dog and looked up almost defiantly.

Fox laughed, not pleasantly. The rumble in the dog's throat grew more menacing.

'So why don't you sell it down-Level and solve all your problems?'

'Wolf's my *friend*,' the boy said, not angrily, just stating a fact.

The woman laughed again, and turned to go.

'Hey –'

She swung around.

'Is it all right if we come back here again to sleep? Please?'

*

She thought she might avoid the place for a few days herself, just in case the boy had any ideas of adopting her as a protector. But something about him had fastened itself to her memory, and she found herself saying to a bartender the night after, 'Do you know a boy, about fifteen or sixteen, a legit, who goes around with a large black dog?'

The bartender looked startled. The assassin never usually spoke to anyone except her customers, except to order a drink. 'Yes.'

'What's he called?'

'Calls himself Mouse. I never heard any other name.' She hesitated, risked it.

'Why?'

Fox had considered this question, briefly. 'Does he sell?'

That was something anyone might want to know, for any of several reasons.

'Not so far as I know.'

'So who does he belong to?'

'No one. That dog of his isn't something you want to get in a fight with. And none of the giants want him.'

The assassin finished her drink as the bartender watched her warily. Though she would not have admitted it, she had an unexpected fondness for the boy. It sounded as if Fox was interested in him, and that was a fate she wouldn't wish on anyone. The boy had survived up till now mostly because he was of no particular interest to anyone – at least, not sufficient to surmount the barrier of that protective shadow with those fearsome teeth.

Fox set down the glass, nodded. 'Another Sevell.'

Someone, a professional contact from the look of him, caught her eye. Deliberately she looked away. She had enough money for the next few days, and she wasn't hungry yet. If he'd been told to find her, he'd wait. If he hadn't, she didn't greatly care. And if he was professional, he'd have more sense than to come up behind her. No one did that twice. When she'd finished the second glass, he was still there, and still trying to catch her eye. She put the glass down, and nodded to him.

He was a professional; he started right. 'My client wants you to kill someone on Level 121,' he said, low, even though the bartender and anyone else in what might possibly be earshot were making it obvious they weren't listening.

Fox considered it. 121 wasn't impossible. 'Who?'

'Her name is Seren Haminh; she lives in Corridor 11, Square 4. Number 23. Here's an image.'

Fox looked at the flat picture, memorising it, in the minute before it ashed unspectacularly to unremarkable dust. 'So. When?'

'Within the next sixty hours.'

The assassin nodded. 'I charge one hundred.'

'Acceptable. Half now, half when?'

'In sixty hours. The *Narrow Room*, Level 278.'

The contact nodded, passed a credit tag unobtrusively across. He left quietly. No one not in the profession would know for sure whether the assassin had accepted or refused the job; and no one except the contact and, in this case, the client, would know for sure exactly who was responsible for the messy death of Seren Haminh, probably about fifty hours from now, when the hunger would be rising again and giving her a few hours to sleep the first ecstasy off.

In the meantime; the boy. Mouse. Fox smiled, bought a unit of Sevell, and left the bar.

*

The boy was asleep, curled up with the dog. Without compunction, Fox kicked him awake.

Mouse – the name did suit him, Fox thought with a private grin – yelped and sat up. 'I didn't – I haven't –

'Remember me?'

The boy rubbed at his face, looked up. 'You said we could sleep here –'

'Wouldn't you rather sleep in a room? No rats, for one thing.'

'I told you,' he said patiently, 'we can't.'

'Suppose we do a deal, Mouse.'

He jerked a little at the sound of his name, and she nodded. 'I know what you are. And I'll tell you, sooner or later it's going to occur to someone you could be useful; useful enough to make it worthwhile taking out that dog. So the deal is this. You rent a room. Legit. I get food. I give you food for you and your mutt, and I sleep in the room.'

'What if I say no?'

For an instant Fox was going to hit the little idiot, but the impulse faded. 'Please yourself. But it's the best offer you're likely to get in a long time.'

The dog was awake by this time, and on its feet, hackles raised. Mouse took its head in his hands and met its eyes, looking at it for a long moment. Then he stood up. 'Yes. All right.'

Fox nodded. 'That's sensible. Come on.'

'What's your name?' Mouse asked, padding along beside her. The dog followed at his heels.

'They call me Fox.'

*

There was a room, with a watertap, free on Level 281. It was exactly three metres by four, the legal minimum for a residential room. Two broad ledges, shelf and bench and bunk, ran from the wall by the door to the opposite wall, and two grimy mattresses lay on them. The watertap, and a basin on the floor beneath it, was next to the heatring on the far end of the righthand bench. Walls and floor and ceiling and benches were all covered in grey soft smooth plastic that against all odds still managed to look grubby.

Mouse looked at the grimy mattresses, and went over to the tap. 'I'll wipe them clean. Unless you want to sleep now?'

Fox shook her head. 'Not just now. There's a foodstall just around the corridor. What does your mutt eat?'

For the first time, Mouse smiled. 'Anything that's not moving too fast.'

Fox came back with three heated packets of 500k mush and a couple of flavour wafers. She handed two packets and a wafer to the boy, who had finished wiping the mattresses down and had leant them up against the wall to dry.

She tipped the contents of one packet into her own messkit and stirred in the crumbled wafer. Looking up, she saw Mouse divide his wafer into two portions, sprinkling one over a flat, battered metal dish for the dog and stirring the other into his own.

'Mouse. Do you seriously believe the mutt tastes what it gulps down? Why waste flavour on it?'

The boy bit his lip, but looked straight at Fox. 'He's not a mutt. His name's Wolf. And we're friends. We share what we have.'

The assassin grinned. 'Friends? How touching. Of course, they say all empaths are half-cracked. Where did you get it?'

'He escaped from Their labs. He's a genetic experiment.'

'So, a mutant. And how do you know?'

Mouse shrugged.

'Made it up, hnh?' The assassin's voice was lazy with contempt.

The dog was snarling low in its throat. Fox flicked a glance at it. 'I should keep a close eye on your . . . *friend*. If it manages to kill me in my sleep one night, you'll be as badly off as you were before.'

'Wolf wouldn't kill you.'

'Oh, you control it even as you sleep?'

'He wouldn't kill you so long as I'm alive. It – it hurts, being around someone who's just killed someone . . . or hurt them. It . . . it's painful.' The empath looked up at Fox as if for help, genuinely puzzled as to how to express his feeling in words.

Fox began to laugh. She finished the brief meal, still amused, and dumped her messkit under the tap. Pulling one mattress onto the ledge, she sat down on it and luxuriously pulled her boots off. 'Keep that *friend* of yours quiet. I'm going to sleep for a few hours.'

She was still not sure why she had made this arrangement. There were other legits she might have bribed or bullied into a similar sharing, but the stairs and the other dusty corners of the World were safer for someone who lived by her knife and her wits. She was certain she could trust this boy, and the very certainty puzzled her. It had nothing to do with his empathy, for shield as deep as she would, until the whole World became flatly three-dimensional, the conviction was still there.

Still, why?

It felt peaceful around him.

That thought nearly shocked Fox fully awake again. She was an assassin – a psychopathic killer. She had nothing to do with peace, neither in life, nor in her anticipated death. But it did feel peaceful, as though, even shielded against him, she could feel the aura of happiness that surrounded him . . . A psychopathic killer had nothing to do with happiness, either. She grinned at the thought, and slid at last into sleep, smiling.

*

Fox woke, and found Mouse kneeling at the basin, rinsing clean both his own messkit and hers. 'You don't have to do that.'

'I don't mind.'

She reached out for the time and found that she had over forty hours still to go before she met the contact again. Allow twelve hours to sleep off the kill, and that left thirty to study the area and make certain there were no surprises. And she would have to buy food now for the boy for the next forty-odd hours, since she'd be in no fit state to do so after.

The hunger was running inside her, a fine, anticipating thread of pleasure. 'I'll be going out. I'll buy some food for you; I won't be back for maybe thirty hours. When I do, I'll want to sleep. Don't disturb me – I'll wake when it's time.'

*

Although Level 121 was manufactory, not a residential two-figure Level, it was low-status enough to include residential areas. Square 4 was one of them. An illegit would be an unusual sight there, Fox untucked her sleeves and pulled them down to hang over her wrists. This might impede her if it came to a fight, but that was unlikely. A gangpath ran from Corridor 11, just by number 23, crossing Corridor 12 high up, and twisting onto one of the stairs.

Prudently, Fox smashed the single working light over the gangpath doorway, and returned to Corridor 11 to watch for her prey.

Seren Haminh was – according to the image – between fifty and sixty years old, of average height, grey-haired and grey-eyed. Her face was pleasant, blandly forgettable; a face worth a fortune.

Three hours later, still waiting, Fox was rerunning her plan of action to check for alternatives. Her contact hadn't said whether Haminh lived alone or not, and without definite information Fox was not about to risk waiting for her inside her room. In any case, she preferred killing grounds with at least two and preferably three escape routes. The stair was perfect.

Except that it if it involved waiting in this corridor for much longer, one of the security cameras might start to register her despite all diversionary moves, and she should therefore now take a break of at least six hours before coming back here.

It annoyed Fox. Shift-change was long over; Haminh should have returned here at least an hour ago, unless she had a lover who hadn't been mentioned, who she was in the habit of spending a shift with. If that was true, it was *really* annoying; a professional contact should take time to find out all the likely addresses for the assassin to check.

At that precise time, she was sitting on a bench in the middle of the corridor, at a carefully calculated point that should be just out of sight from the security cameras at either side. The camera across the corridor could see her, but at that range would be unable to focus on detail. Her clothing was standard-issue, anyway. She was glancing through a newssheet that she had looked through already a dozen times and that in any case told nothing particularly interesting.

A tweak at the edge of her consciousness said: *prey*.

She looked up. The crowds had lessened considerably, and a woman slightly shorter than Fox, grey-haired, was approaching the door of number 23. Fox slipped delicately into her mind, confirming that this was Seren Haminh, and stood up, dropping the newssheet into a wastebin nearby. Casually, keeping a light touch on Haminh's mind, she wandered over to the metal ramp that led up to the residential walkway, encouraging Haminh with light touches to turn into the gangpath instead of walking straight past to her own doorway.

It was so easy. She sometimes wondered how assassins who weren't telepathic managed it.

Haminh didn't panic until she was past Corridor 12 and Fox drew close enough behind her to be heard. The assassin gave her no time to cry out; a flare of terror – *what am I doing here who is that behind me dark dark someone behind me* – and Fox tightened her hold on the other's mind, taking control. It was so easy. It was only the killing that was hard.

Each time, even when the hunger ran swift and compelling through her, each time she had to compel her hands to take hold of her prey's neck and kill. Best of all when they died in her hands.

In the instant of death, though, it changed.

And Seren Haminh, in the instant before dissolution, saw and knew and understood that she was dying utterly and completely and forever, as the shock and agony and terror screamed to infinite depths, Fox linked and shared, high and higher.

No human is capable of truly knowing that they are not immortal, that someday the *I* that seemed eternal will cease, save in one moment; the moment before true death. And always, always, however she killed, the moment of agonising red pleasure that was awareness of non-existence, the *I* stilled, the beautiful blissful moment when she did not exist and they did not exist and They did not exist and the whole dusty lightless World was not – only the certainty of not-existing never lasted and soon she would have to kill again. And again, forever.

*

She came out of the bliss eternities later.

Timesense told her it had been barely fifteen seconds. The corpse's bracelet was beginning to squeal; Fox dragged it off and flung it down the stairwell; she didn't hear it land.

She went up the stairs two Levels, dodged across a gangpath to another stair and went up that five Levels, and finally, across another gangpath and she leapt for a lift just leaving.

Still on autopilot, she left the lift two Levels below 281, and went unstoppably through the narrow sideways and gangpaths until she reached the room. She fell down on the mattress and went instantly to death.

*

Mouse had been curled up with Wolf on one of the mattresses, sleepily combing the tangled hair of Wolf's great mane with his fingers, when the sandy-haired woman slammed through the door and kicked it shut behind her. Wolf was awake, instantly, and instantly into a fighting stance; but Fox only collapsed to the othèr mattress, and lay there, still.

She was dead, the boy knew with certainty, but just as certainly he could feel the pulse of her living, sickeningly ragged, horribly dead. Unalive. Undead.

The pulse was dragging him in, into that horrid rhythm, now dead, now living. Red, black. Red, black. Red. Black. Red. Black.

With an incoherent whimper, Mouse rolled himself to Wolf, pulling his protector to him. Burying his face into the warm living darkness of Wolf's fur, he tried desperately to wall away the sickening pulse. Red. Black. Red. Black. Red Black RedBlackRedBlack

Moaning, Mouse surrendered.

*

He was in there, in the red darkness, trapped. With Fox he clung eagerly, sickened at his/her eagerness, to the scarlet deadness, knowing he/she did not exist, was not, was nothing, and nothing was, only red, cold empty red forever. And then, with terror that was not his own, he was alive again, in the sweet blackness, and Mouse clung desperately, only to be wrenched back to the red deathly peace, hearing an endless scream as a woman he had never seen died, died endlessly and *now*.

*

In the stretched moments when he could think at all, Mouse knew, helplessly, that he was going mad. To be near someone who had just killed was painful, agonising if the killer had enjoyed the killing. But this – was as though Fox had died and was still dying, and had enjoyed her own kill. . . .

The red death returned and for an eternity he was nothing at all.

Blackness, warm and friendly as Wolf's fur, the only warmth he'd ever had. And far far away in the blackness, Wolf's deep bark.

The sound was like a lifeline. Desperately he clung to it unable to bear even the thought of the nothingness again, and felt Fox's fury lash against him. Even enduring anger was better than the redness, even anger aimed by a telepath.

How can a telepath kill?

No answer, only formless rage, and a fierce longing.

How can you kill, when you die with them?

And finally an answer, contemptuous, but speech: *I like dying*.

He could hear Wolf in the blackness, coming closer, and

knew he must distract Fox from hearing his approach, or Fox would drag them both back into the redness.

What is there to like? It's nothing!

Nothing, yes! *Ahh –*

And Wolf was on them, his swift silver presence a compact laserbolt, seizing Mouse and pulling. Out of the blackness, away from the redness, safe home. And Fox with them. She screamed, a cry that seemed not to come from a human throat, a deathyell of mortal agony and longing.

*

Mouse was lying half on and half off the mattress, his face buried in Wolf's coat, making small whimpering noises in his throat. Wolf was licking him as though he were a very small puppy. The room was silent, utterly silent and still.

The boy shifted over. Fox lay on her back, her arms thrown out above her head, her face distorted by the scream. She was barely breathing. Even as he sat up, though, she rolled over and sprang, straight for his throat, her mind incandescent with rage, her mindvoice screaming threats and curses and obscenities, coloured all with a hungry pleasure that sickened Mouse; *Die! Die, you little empath ratson fatherfucker mindsucker die –*

Her hands had begun to tighten around his neck, when abruptly two things happened at once. The horrible delight that held Mouse paralysed, sweeping to a climax, changed without warning to a tidal wave of nausea. And Wolf's jaws closed on Fox's throat. *All very well,* said Wolf, *but you die too.*

Fox jolted back on her heels, dropping Mouse. The nausea was swallowed, absorbed in a flood of surprise and shock.

'A telepathic dog?' Her voice sounded rusty.

Wolf was still watching her, carefully, but Mouse stood up. 'Wolf, she won't hurt us,' aware that he was repeating himself. He filled the cup from Fox's messkit and brought it over to her.

She took it, staring now from Wolf to Mouse and back again, and drank. *He knew I was thirsty. And the mutt is –*

I'm not telepathic. And I'm not a mutt. I'm a telekineticist.

'Of course, that explains everything,' Fox said with irony.

Mouse flopped down on the floor and started to giggle. With a snarl, Fox spun around and slapped him, harder than necessary. Almost the last thing she wanted to deal with was a hysterical empath.

She felt the slap across her own face. Wolf's muzzle flinched. 'I'm shielding from you. Damn you, how did you broadcast that through my shields –'

I didn't, Mouse said inside Fox's mind. *Use your own senses. You can't shield from me any more. And I can't from you. And nor can Wolf.*

Fox closed her shields down, tighter and harder than ever before, so that even her timesense was cut off, but still, now that Mouse had betrayed it, still she could feel the shimmery fragile links running between her and this stupid lackwit empath, this mutant mongrel animal –

'You're linked yourself,' she said aloud, almost spitting it. '*Perverts.* You're *friends*? Hey, maybe I should make a visicord of you two, sell it down-Level, sell you two down-Level to a doghouse where they do that kind of thing! You'd be great entertainment!'

You can't deny we're linked, said Wolf inside her mind.

Fox's mouth twisted. 'I can break the link. It's no beginning bond.'

Wolf did not speak. He only curled up, laying his head down on his forepaws, looking up at Fox with mocking amusement clear in one tilted eye.

Biting in what she might have said, she stood, and strode over to the door. 'Fox!' Mouse sounded terrified. 'Where are you going?'

She spun around, grinning triumphantly at him. 'Sit there and wonder, empath. I tell you I can break this bond, and maybe I will this time and leave you to starve, and maybe I won't, maybe I'll leave that pleasure for another time. You and your mutt can rot and die as soon as this arrangement stops being worthwhile for me.'

Aren't you curious?

Wolf's sendings were like quicksilver. Fox held herself tautly controlled, turning again and leaving, closing the door behind her. Timesense said she had maybe three hours to reach the *Narrow Room*.

*

The contact paid her fifty credits, with approval for a job efficiently done in the shape of a glass of Sevell. Then he made the small finger-gesture, as among professionals, for 'switching clients'. 'My client wants you to kill someone –'

The sickness engulfed her again. Fox shook her head.

He was a professional; he didn't ask why.

'I'm retiring,' Fox said, realising that she hadn't expected to say that. 'That was my last job.' *I killed. They killed the hunger.*

Standing up, she looked down at him. He was a professional; but she was no longer of that profession. 'From now on,' said the telepath, very quietly, 'I only kill people who get in my way.'

Most unprofessional

*

She was on the lift up before she realised where she was going. Back to that small room where the mutant dog with the quicksilver mindvoice and the small quiet empath lay, she knew, tangled with each other in sleep. *Curious? Yes.* But already she knew what it was like to be going home.

Being Here

WALTER PERRIE

The first sections, from my commonplace-book, provide a kind of background for the reflections which follow.

Cruising

I MOVE from game to game with increasing abruptness. For all that I have learned a greater variety of games, there are fewer I can tolerate. Perhaps this is evident to (at least some) others and thereby creates a reciprocal intolerance. Wherever the game is, is home; so one plays the sauna like poker, with narrowing intensity. The air is heavy enough for the ambiguities to be all in the skill of the players. Bars are less demanding. One may go simply *pour passer le soir*. Streets or parks are too theatrical for me to be at ease, so I make bad moves, exaggerate or, more often, under-bid.

I understand, I think, Auden's obsessive home-making ritual in 'About the House': new location, old rules.

> the houses of our City
> are real enough but they lie
> haphazardly scattered over the earth,
> and her vagabond forum is any space

where two of us happen to meet
who can spot a citizen
without papers. So, too, can her foes.
Where the power lies
remains to be seen.

In the games I enjoy, the better I become at them, the more do they come to resemble dream; and the more does sleep-dream seem familiar, comfortable, homely. That dream world has more solidity than a house uninhabited.

Transitions within a game to a different stage or to another game entirely are the moments of maximum vulnerability: from look to touch; from touch to speech — speech the most difficult of all. The game to game move, if the most dangerous, is also the most exhilarating since, in the moment of transition, it offers the unknown, escape from the familiar. Travel is cheaper.

Glasgow 1978

There are three bars within a hundred yards of each other. I caught him watching me in the third. Later I realised he had also been in the other two. Not my type. Heavy-set, short, unshaven, sullen-looking. Closing time. I waited twenty minutes in Glasgow drizzle and still no bus. From the top of Hope Street I took a short-cut across the waste-land surrounding the motorway. He came from behind me, his right arm across my neck. In his left hand a short piece of rough wood with a razor-blade stuck in the end. Whatever musings had abstracted me from the charms of the city fled before the lucidity of that long-drawn-out instant of disaster. Unable to resist the opportunity to gloat, or realise his fantasies in language, he paused:

'Ah'm gonnae cut ye up, ya fuckin' queer.'

The blade was about two inches from my left eye. I grabbed his wrist, twisting the hand away from my face. I smelled sweat and the drink on his breath. He was much heavier than I. We struggled and I fell, still holding the hand away. He stood in a semi-crouch and laid-in with a boot, twice, then slipped and fell beside me. I got up and sprinted the 150 yards or so. The shoplights, streetlamps, a few pedestrians were now only yards away. In a state of aerial calm I stopped to see whether he was following. He was but stopped and stared at me, then turned and ran in the opposite direction.

Next evening, bruised and with minor cuts and a cracked arm, I forced myself to go back to the three bars though, by then, very nervous. In the struggle I had lost a scarf I valued but never went back for it.

Vancouver 1985

He invited me into his cubicle with a gesture. He was handsome, perhaps twenty-three or four, slim, fine-featured and with a shock of pale brown hair. His desire was extraordinarily intense. He thought it was for sex. Nor did he wish for any reciprocal act. Afterwards we sat on the palette, facing each other, sharing the obligatory cigarette. We exchanged names. Without warning, tears began to roll down his cheeks.

He began to sob and then shudder under the weight of his grief. Appalled by such nakedness, I held him. When, finally, he had stilled, his despair and self-possession were tangible as the squalor of the place. We sat looking at each other, he still holding my hand. The emotion he generated about him in those moments was a pit of black silence. I felt entirely useless. I asked if he would like a coffee, or to be taken home, but he could only shake his head. Soon I left him to sleep.

Aberdeen 1966

The hotel seemed deserted. It was after eleven and everyone had gone to bed. I sat reading in the lounge-bar. Peter came in and began to chat me up. He bought me a brandy. I was unaccustomed to alcohol. He asked me to his room. We had been exchanging enthusiasms for Italian opera and I was enticed by his collection of Caruso recordings. I was too inexperienced and nervous to understand the obviousness of his approach. Nevertheless, he was patient and, eventually, I got my act together and spent the night with him. For days afterwards anxiety and guilt were on the table for lunch and self-contempt at my own cowardice in avoiding him provided supper. The issue was resolved by an act of quarantine. By day, nothing had happened. Only in the imaginings of the night, in reverie devoted exclusively to sexual touch was anything resembling recognition possible. So all real context was gradually stripped from sex and sexual imagination. It became the leper of a consciousness playing the moral majority. There were in my fantasies no moments of tenderness or anger, accommodations, reconciliations, no traffic, no shoppers, no birds, no intrusions. Only the warm envelope of fantasy and the intensities isolation afforded. What little self-confidence I had ever had packed its bags and left and an aggressive dogmatism and snobbery moved in. The vital thing was not to lose face.

Edinburgh 1977

I am standing on a mountain ledge at night. Above me, a precipice of unbroken rock. Below me, darkness. Before me, on the ledge, a circular stone tower. My younger brother is holding my left hand but he is only vaguely present, shadowy. There is a door at the base of the tower. We go in. The interior is a single room, lofty, bright and circular, paved with grey stone flags. Into recesses in the wall are set a range of marvellous and enigmatic gadgets, clearly the products of some sophisticated science. These objects are also simple and beautiful. In one recess is the structure of a rectangular solid; that is, only the defining edges of the solid exist. Within the box, suspended at its centre, glows a point of brilliant, pale-blue light.

At the far end of the room is a medieval canopy of the type seen in the *Book of Hours* of the Duc du Berry. From within the canopy a man steps out towards us. He is perhaps in his middle-fifties, silver-haired, authoritative. He is dressed in a gown of pale-blue, embroidered in silver and gold with astrological and alchemical symbols. He offers us revelation.

My shadow-brother is afraid and runs away. The man takes my hands in his and places them within the box and around the point of life.

We are standing outside the tower on the ledge. Before us the entire universe is spread out like a bolt of black silk unfurled. Uncountable galaxies spiral before us, receding in linear perspective to a single flux of light. The vision is both intensely beautiful and melancholy, with the tone of Beethoven's *Heilige Dankgesang*. He still holds my hands but has become younger and dark-haired. There are tears in his eyes. He kisses me and I understand that this age is passing away, this universe.

Now I am on the tower's battlements, which are square. All the stars are extinguished, dead. Below the tower, clouds swirl across a grey moonscape lit from moment to moment by volcanic fires. Apocalypse. With me on the battlements are several nuns and Dominican monks. In the centre of the square, a second canopy from which emerges a young woman carrying a stave. The stave is budded and sports a few leaves as in some versions of the tarot. She is dressed hippie-style in jeans and shirt. Her long, pale-brown hair reaches to her waist. Over her left shoulder she carries a shoulder-bag. She hands the stave to me. I believe it to be the source of evil.

I touch the tip of the stave to the centre of her forehead. A tiny point of bright golden pus appears and spreads like some fierce eczema down and across the right-hand side of her face. She draws a small rectangular mirror from her shoulder-bag and watches as the pus begins to consume the left-hand side of her face. She begins to scream and, running to the edge of the battlements, throws herself into the precipice. I chase each of the monks and nuns round the canopy until all have been similarly consumed and thrown themselves over the battlements; for who can bear to lose face?

Edinburgh 1984

The minuet was not more measured. I saw him as I rounded the corner; *very* handsome, expensively dressed, a casualness no European can muster. He was on the other side of the road, saw me watching him, stopped, turned and walked slowly for fifty yards in the direction he had come. I walked on for perhaps forty yards and stopped, lighting a cigarette and looking vaguely in his direction. He crossed the road to walk past me, slowly; another fifty yards. He turned as though suddenly remembering something, returned, passing me again and stopping on the next corner. I followed. He grinned: 'Hi.'

Edinburgh (undated)

Only once have the gods assaulted me in the guise of another person. I was leaving an office in a busy New Town square. It was a drizzling spring afternoon and I paused on the steps to button my coat. Among the crowd of pedestrians I glimpsed a creature, whether boy or girl, and suddenly had the breath taken from me as though I had been punched, hard. I just stood, gawking and shivering, as it disappeared into the hurrying crowd.

Seattle 1985

Silent, face down in the half-light, the black boy writhes hips and spine, serpentine, oiled, musculature moving as in dance, inviting a cock to complete him, counterpoint his *eros* of motion with some simpler, maybe brutal, theme. He does not look round. Wanting what? Not a person but some essence of person, person distilled and condensed into simply *cock*, without profession or prejudice, unremembering: a human blank to be filled in by whatever image of selfhood and otherness will be satisfied in that strangest, most complete of intimacies.

Why should there be a surface to get beneath, a skin to get under? The skin is its own sense-organ. Behind the eye, inside the tongue. Why look for dis-assembly? But at what point in the isolation of elements does a person become merely a mad torso with head attached? In that refusal of personhood to moments of partiality is the hidden root of fascism. We fear such moments, not trusting the body: for the forgetting is only a game. What are the spasms of the bathhouse but acts of quarantine, moments of salvation in the myriad hells of conformity, and overriding all, the insistence that we be 'integrated', 'responsible', 'whole'. Let the mad torso have its moment.

'But how can you be like that?'

'How can I not?'

*

Reflections

There is a commonplace error which speaks of the 'contradictions' in society. But there are no contradictions in experience, only in propositions about experience, which is to say, in discourse and especially in ideological discourse. What is alluded to is *conflict* and the civilisation we live in — Scotland in the 1980s — is rife with it. You need only set up elegantly simple categories and logic will whisk you to whatever conclusion you have in mind. But the resolution of conflict in experience can tolerate formal contradiction. It is the living-through complexity which is the interesting bit. In ideology the individual disappears behind the mask of category or type. What I mean may be clearer after some autobiographical reflections.

Unfortunately, I am old enough to recall, vividly, the years before 'gay liberation' was ever heard of in Scotland. There were then no consenting adults, only criminals, even if the 'crimes' were usually victimless. For his pains my first bedmate could have had the benefits of a protracted rest in one of our quaint medieval prisons. So marked were my anxieties that I buried that experience for several years. The interment was, however, in a shallow grave and the corpse far from extinct, so I, for my pains, was haunted.

The well-fleshed ghosts of my imaginings were like the insistent *daimones* of classical times who, if neglected, drove their victim to ever-greater follies. And so it was. Eventually, *in extremis,* I poured the appropriate libations and: it worked — or seemed to. Certainly, it brought about the beginnings of an emotional freedom I had not known, and a deeper commitment to radical politics. But the *Erinyes* are not so easily bought off, for what seemed so cleanly available was too lucid, too crisply dialectical.

If wholesale confusion and evasion had given way to a world of possible action and satisfaction, nothing else had been transformed. Years of self-deception are not so easily washed away in evangelical frenzy. The undeveloped soul, still in its infancy, thirsts for Absolutes after its years in the desert. And what mischief and damage will an uncurbed and inexperienced Ariel not do? Absolutes, like the categories on which they browse, are all-too-simple creatures. And they are never at ease with each other. Any two in one place is a certain cue for conflict. In the blue corner: life as she could, should and ought to be. In the red: life as she is.

My earliest years were spent in a small, close-knit, Lanarkshire mining community in which class boundaries were as clearly drawn as the boundaries of the surrounding fields. There were a few catholic families but the majority and the consensus derived from presbyterian Scottish/Ulster stock. Sex, far less homosexuality, was a topic I never heard discussed by adults.

I now live in a small Perthshire village, substantially less homogeneous than the one in which I grew up but in which there are also a few catholic families and where the majority are of presbyterian Scottish/Ulster stock. There are no blacks, no Jews and, of course, no homosexuals — at least, not publicly. I should add that I had some entertainment on learning that not so long ago the local minister had run off with a young man. But even in Scotland, times change. Even allowing for a more diverse class-composition, this village inhabits another world from that other. The fact that the media regularly confront their audience with discourse and images about gays requires that a vocabulary for dealing with such awkwardnesses be discovered, even if it be the lexicon of bigotry and stereotype. By and large, people still prefer *not* to acknowledge these issues for which there is no comfortable rule. Traditional reticences though are being broken down. That may, in some respects, be healthy but it also has to be said that those reticences marked a division between private and public spheres which may have made compromise possible. Tact, in eighties Britain, has become an affectation.

To some it will seem perverse to choose to inhabit that village-world of rural prejudice but I was never a town-child and the Scottish cities in particular hold no charms for me. The days of casual sex from encounters in bars and discos went out with the arrival of AIDS, at least as a way of life. Nor would there be any point in living in such a village unless one were largely prepared to conform to its *public* mores since otherwise one could not be within the community in any real sense. The price one pays is circumspection. A zealot's life is not a happy one.

Even in the best of times Scotland is a neurotic sort of place. Its national confusions and insecurities are legion. And the effort to remain emotionally, morally or intellectually well can itself be crippling. But fiery activism or evasive quiescence are the poles of choice and the poles are notoriously uninhabitable. What one chooses must depend on where and who and what one is: have you somewhere to live, a job, how much education have you, a lover to offer support, a family? *Of itself,* sexual preference is not a sufficiently crucial characteristic to make it very attractive as a graven image.

Floating Off To Timor

EDWIN MORGAN

If only we'd been strangers
we'd be floating off to Timor,
we'd be shimmering on the Trades
in a blue jersey boat
with shandies, flying-fish,
a pace of dolphins
to the copra ports.
And it's no use crying
to me, What dolphins?
I know where they are
and I've have snapped you up
and carried you away
snapped you up
and carried you away
if we had been strangers.

But here we are care
of the black roofs.
It's not hard to find
with a collar turned up
and a hoot from the Clyde.
The steps come home
whistling too. And a kettle

steams the cranes out slowly.
It's living with ships
makes a rough springtime
and who is safe
when they sing and blow
their music — they seem
to swing at some light rope
like those desires
we keep for strangers.
God, the yellow deck
breathes, it heaves spray
back like a shout.
We're cutting through
some straits of the world
in our old dark room
with salty wings
in the shriek of the dock wind.
But we're caught — meshed
in the fish-scales, ferries,
mudflats, lifebelts
fading into football cries
and the lamps coming on
to bring us in.

We take in
the dream, a cloth from the line
the trains fling sparks on
in our city. We're better awake.
But you know I'd take
you all the same,
if you were my next stranger.

From A City Balcony

Edwin Morgan

How often when I think of you the day grows bright!
Our silent love
wanders in Glen Fruin with butterflies and cuckoos —
bring me the drowsy country thing! Let it drift above the
traffic
by the open window with a cloud of witnesses —
a sparkling burn, white lambs, the blaze of gorse,
the cuckoos calling madly, the real white clouds over us,
white butterflies about your hand in the short hot grass,
and then the witness was my hand closing on yours,
my mouth brushing your eyelids and your lips
again and again till you sighed and turned for love.
Your breast and thighs were blazing like the gorse.
I covered your great fire in silence there.
We let the day grow old along the grass.
It was in the silence the love was.

Footsteps and witnesses! In this Glasgow balcony who pours
such joy like mountain water? It brims, it spills over and
over
down to the parched earth and the relentless wheels.

How often will I think of you, until
our dying steps forget this light, forget
that we ever knew the happy glen,
or that I ever said, We must jump into the sun,
and we jumped into the sun.

Mine Own Nature

Alex Rainbow

Alice

I THINK I must have been slightly mad for most of my life. I have certainly been screaming with loneliness for as long as I can remember. I was born into a working-class family in the West of Ireland. Being the only girl in a family of seven was bad enough but there were no other girls anywhere near my age in our local area either, though of course I went to an all-girl convent school.

I was very tomboyish and my parents allowed me a great deal of freedom until that magic day came when I was supposed to become 'a little lady'. Prior to my fifteenth birthday I had asked for train sets and cowboy suits for Xmas and birthdays, and until I was eighteen I spent Saturday afternoons making tea and sandwiches for my Mam and some girls from school as they talked endlessly of 'fellas' and clothes and make-up — subjects never of any interest to me. The obsession of my life was, and partly still is, the whole phenomenon of sex, of gender. Why only two sexes? Why not one, or three, or ten? Best of all why not none? Why only two sexes and why is the female sex oppressed in every culture on this planet? When, as a teenager, I read D. H. Lawrence's poem 'The Tortoise', the line 'O why are we crucified into sex at all?'seemed to me the most basic and profound of all existential cries. I brooded constantly over why my being a girl rather than a boy would make my life so different from my brothers'. It was always assumed that they would get a job, a home, a wife and children, in that order. It seemed they could have everything merely because they were boys, they would not have to sacrifice anything for anything else. I, however, could only be a nun like my aunt or I could be like my Mam. My Mam was a very attractive, passionate, extrovert womon who lived her life for my Dad and for all of us. Unremitting poverty, seven children and a husband unable to do hard physical work because of a series of minor heart attacks, caused my Mam to have a 'mental breakdown' when I was seven years old; the treatment for this breakdown included her having twenty electric shocks in a two-year period. Her life was a ceaseless round of hard work, of struggling to make ends meet, of keeping up appearances and yet her lion-like spirit showed through. My Mam was 'the boss' at home but outside that house she was merely a wife and mother, never a person in her own right.

I would have cut my throat rather than grow up to be like my Mam. Being a nun seemed a far more satisfying life than being a wife and mother. To all of us school-girls the convent seemed a beautiful, exciting place and the nuns simultaneously frightening and glamorous. I was always attracted by the lifestyle of a nun, particularly that of a contemplative. The options of married life and spiritual life were the only ones open to us. As the nuns themselves often said to us: 'Girls, a single person is useless to God and country.' I always knew I would be such a useless person . . .

When I was ten years old the first sensational accounts of 'sex-changes' appeared in the Sunday papers. They were all men who became psuedo-wimmin. The first time I read about a sex change something happened deep inside me: all my vague feelings about being a girl found a focus even though all the stories were about men who became 'wimmin'. It was all so simple. I would become a boy. When I grew up I would become a man in the way that other girls would become nurses or teachers or whatever. My obsession took root then. I kept a secret scrapbook throughout my teens of every sex-change report in the papers. Since I was ten years old I walked about our little town mentally transforming every womon I saw into a man and every man into a womon. I looked at myself in shop windows and mentally transformed the self that I was, a girl in a dress with ribbons in her hair, into the self I would become, a muscular man on a motorbike wearing a leather jacket. When I was ten years old somehow choosing to be a boy seemed a good idea, a logical plan to follow. From being a child to being an adult this apparent choice changed to the overriding, deep-rooted belief that I was actually a boy, that nature had somehow made a mistake biologically but that I was really a boy. I lived only for the day when I would come into my own.

From when I was eleven years old I felt totally alone. I had had one very close childhood friend, Maeve, but her family had moved to a different part of the country and I never saw her again.

There was never anybody I could talk to about my transsexual feelings. I kept them to myself, where they constantly grew in depth and where they became merely a backdrop to my private obsession: home, family, school, everything. A transvestite is somebody who wears the clothes of the other sex — in our society it is considered bizarre for men to wear wimmin's clothing, though it is now common for wimmin to wear men's clothing. A transsexual is somebody who actually wants to be the other totally . . . I wanted to be a man in every way.

I knew my family would never accept me as a boy or man, so I began to withdraw from them. It was pointless making friends who would reject the 'new me' in the future, so I stopped making friends. I went through everyday life merely marking time until I could leave Ireland for Britain to become the real me. To keep my distance from everybody, always being a polite child, I became an unusually polite teenager. I knew I would be alone all my life so I started preparing for it as soon as possible. I read a lot as a child, but as a teenager I read every book in our local library. I was at the local convent school from twelve to eighteen years old and I was considered clever but 'strange'. My habit of going for long walking and cycling trips alone further exacerbated my reputation for oddness. As my transsexual obsession deepened I was prone to bouts of morbid depression and I spent a great deal of time thinking about suicide; suicide was almost a twin obsession at times.

Always conscious of the power in female-male relationships, I was bitterly aware of my own inferior position in the scheme of things. Five of my brothers are older than me and one younger. Relatives always made disparaging remarks about me 'breaking the chain' of five boys, but consoled my parents that they at least had a girl to look after them in their old age. My brothers were always called 'fine, handsome boys' while 'the little girl is nice'. My self-loathing deepened all the time. I felt totally alienated from my body, the inferior female body that labelled me second-rate, the body that I did not ask to have. I have never questioned my sexuality. I have always been exclusively attracted to girls and wimmin in any sexual or deep emotional way; it has always been a part of me as grey eyes or dark hair. All the time I was growing up I had never heard the word 'homosexual' or even jokes about 'queers'. I think my transsexual obsession must have triggered puberty when I could not reconcile the fact of my being a girl with my intense crushes on other girls. Only if I were a boy could I ask girls out on dates; only if I were a boy could I have sexual contact with girls. It never occurred to me that somewhere wimmin might love other wimmin precisely because they were other wimmin and that this love could include a sexual dimension.

The year I was eighteen I left our town for college. I had a place to study engineering, my major in electronics. I made no friends or even close acquaintances during my eighteen months at college. There were about ten girls on the engineering course but I kept entirely to myself.

My perennial thoughts of transsexualism and suicide never left me, but in many ways I was happier than I had ever been in my life. However, financial problems, ever-increasing feelings of personal isolation and frustration, and constant pressure to give up something like engineering, forced me to leave college halfway through the course. Eventually, I got a job as bank clerk in London when the banks went on a recruiting drive in Ireland. So, aged twenty, I finally left Kerry for London to begin my transformation into a man.

For the next ten years I lived in London. It was like a vast playground to me, full of excitement and interest. I loved the anonymity of London; nobody bothered me. I lived near one of my brothers, but I was still alone as always. The first year was a magical mystery tour. I went to my first gay pub. Although it was mostly men I felt totally at home. I loved the whole ambience. After years of immersing myself in a new culture, I went to my local GP with a long letter explaining my wish to see a psychiatrist. He referred me to the first of several psychiatrists I was to visit for a year. All this was merely a convention as far as I was concerned, an exercise I had anticipated for nearly ten years. I knew the questions they would ask me. I emphasised my 'masculine' traits, ignored any aspects of my interests to temperament which could be termed remotely 'feminine'. I glowed when they gave me their expert opinion that I was in most respects 'a normal young man'. My motto became: 'I am really a man trapped in a womon's body.'

In the beginning they offered me aversion therapy but I furiously refused that. I continually demanded my right to have hormone treatment and operations, to become a man physically as much as possible. When all this was going on I left my job as a bank clerk to work as a messenger. Finally I got my long-awaited appointment to see Dr John Randell, the 'patron saint of transsexuals'. Dr Randell was blunt. Current medical technology could never make me a man in full fact, but I could have what was available. I accepted his offer as Sir Galahad must have accepted the Holy Grail. I left my job to sign on. I moved from my little flat to join a transsexual community, people the other way round to me — men to psuedo-wimmin — but who understood me. I stayed at home as much as possible while I took massive doses of testosterone, the male hormone. The risk of liver cancer associated with this did not bother me in the slightest;

I would have done anything to get what I wanted. I wore a corset over my breasts for a manly appearance. It hurt at first. Next, I went to the barber's for a crew-cut. I bought a man's tweed jacket, trousers and suit. I registered my new name, Alan, with the local DHSS. During this time I tried to avoid going out. People often asked me the time just to hear my voice so they could proclaim my gender to their friends. I was unable to use the public toilets since I was told I was in the wrong one whichever I went to.

Gradually I put on body weight, a lot of it muscle bulk, and took to daily weight training. My voice deepened. I grew sideburns. I looked and talked like a lad of sixteen instead of a womon of twenty-two. I was ready to fulfil the condition of my having the operation: I had to spend a year 'passing' as a male in stereotypical working-class jobs.

I formed a real friendship with the transvestite man who owned the house where I lived. His room was the most interesting I had been in up to then. Books dealing mainly with science and the occult lined the walls, bits of engineering projects littered the table, his ultra-feminine dresses hung in one corner and the printing press of the transsexual/transvestite magazine he edited was in the other corner. Daily life at home was often like a scene from the Rocky Horror Picture Show with transvestites and transsexuals continually visiting. We were often hassled by the neighbours and occasionally by the police. Verbal abuse on the streets was commonplace, a brick through the window was not unusual. Every day I ventured forth on my series of jobs: guard on the railway, driver's mate, window cleaner, warehouse assistant. I was always on my guard, always playing the 'macho' role but always worried sick in case I was found out. Probably the worst day of that year, though a typical one, was a particularly hot day in August. I was working with three men at a warehouse near the airport. We were lifting metal girders onto a lorry and securing them in place with wooden slats which we nailed together. As the day wore on the men stripped to the waist in the burning sun. I, however, had to keep wearing my jacket because of my pullover, because of my shirt, because of my corset . . . Amazingly, during this trial year nobody ever suspected that I was a womon, though I occasionally got called 'poofter'.

I had my double masectomy when I was twenty-three. It is a painful operation. Regardless of how I feel about it now, this period was one of the happiest times of my life. Having my breasts removed was having my stigmata removed, the outer visible sign of my inner affliction of inferiority. About eighteen months after my masectomy I had my hysterectomy, an even more painful operation. Between these operations I did occasional voluntary work, mainly on an archaeological site. I had full acceptance as a man. After a TOPS course I got a full-time job in computing and I moved to a different part of London. I was beginning to realise that I would never actually be a man and I already had experienced what I probably wanted more than anything else — the power men have in society. Moreover, there was the sheer pain of the future operations, to permanently deepen my voice and to have my pelvic basin altered to narrow my hips for that distinctively masculine appearance. Surgical techniques for an artificial penis and scrotum were still experimental and any success there seemed a long way in the future. Consequently, I decided I would be an androgynous sort of person and I found old esoteric idea about being a whole person in the alchmeical or shamanic sense, a female-male composite, increasingly attractive. I stopped taking my testosterone tablets and went back on the dole again.

A year later my life changed radically. I was twenty-seven and working in a food and book collective. I read *Gyn/Ecology* by Mary Daly, followed immediately by *The Transsexual Empire* by Janice Raymond. I locked myself for two days and nights in my room without food or water or sleep. I was weeping bitterly for most of the time. I could not talk. I was eating the mat on the floor. I had no self. I lost my identity. I was nobody.

I was a traitor to half the human species — my own half of the human species. The oppression and suffering of wimmin in every culture throughout the millennia overwhelmed me. The links between what the medical profession had done to me in British patriarchy and the cruelties and outrages perpetuated by every patriarchy throughout the world were glaringly obvious. The most obvious, though inadequate, analogy I could think of for my situation was to be a light-skinned black person who identified with white people all her life, who had 'passed' as a white person for years and who had suddenly discovered the reality of Black Power. For a while my self-loathing and judgement of self went deeper than they had ever been in my life. When I came out of my room again I had a new identity, I was a new person. I was a lesbian feminist. I changed my first name because I actually felt I was a new person. I changed my surname because I did not want my sire's name. I wanted my own name because we as wimmin never have our own last names. I felt as though I had been reincarnated in the same lifetime.

That radical change was six years ago. I sometimes find it difficult to believe that other lesbians will accept me as one of them. I realise I am an obsessive sort of person and I realise I may never totally overcome my transsexual feelings. I spend most of my life trying to ingratiate myself into a sick society rather than trying to smash that society. My anger against the medical profession is incalculable: they act as direct agents of the state in 'changing' deviant wimmin and men into people who conform to gender stereotypes. There is a painting by Richard Hamiton of an IRA prisoner in his H-Block cell, his eyes fanatical, his hair long and unkempt, the walls smeared with his own excrement. He is in prison for committing violent crimes against English imperialism and he is demanding status as a political prisoner. Perhaps no other way will I and all the rest of us have the freedom and justice and equality that is ours by right.

No matter how misguided my past, I am a womon. It is written in every cell of my body and, most of all, in thirty years of oppression.

The Other

BRYAN ALLAN

THE ROAD was hidden slightly at the bend, behind the overhang of the rowan trees and they came across the barred gate a little too quickly, crossing the bridge before realising that it was now behind. The car was brought to a sudden halt; an inertial throw, catch, jerkiness unsettled the passengers; fortunately their bodies responded safely. Now the reverse gear was selected, urged into place with a slight rocking motion and the car travelled backwards before hesitantly coming to rest. It stopped adjacent to a fire-notice where a handcrafted firebroom leant, in a forlorn state, mockingly even, tied together with nothing but parcel-string. The car occupants did not move at first, a rising condensation choked the dying ventilation, the inside of the windscreen visibly clouded to reveal nothing more than a general silhouette of the two figures in the front seat deliberating their actions. First one, then the other gingerly descended and as the one with the keys circled the car, checking each orifice and lock, the other brazenly mounted the bonnet and cast his arms and gaze further, far across to the disappearing outline of the receding crag of hill. Not content with his careful appraisal of eye, he produced from his rather torn and shabby coat, a small movie camera and proceeded to set up shot after shot of a narrow-gauge narrative. Meanwhile the other seemed to have finished his duties and was waiting patiently for the movie-person to regain a most equitable composure. Then at the appropriate moment, he unfurled a battered black umbrella, shielding his camera as he came down from the car. At that moment, a lorry thundered by, giving the pair a blast of greeting before disappearing out of sight round a corner. It was the weekly delivery, the lifeline to this scattered old community of not more than five hundred souls all told, set in all these millions of hectares. How the lineage stretched back, back beyond even the advent of written records. A shared memory, a common heritage noted the changes and transformations from the wild pine of old Caledonia, the runic Earragh gaidheal to the new cash-crop of settler plantations.

The wooden trellised gate blocked the way, the outside public highway was detached from the ancient bridle path, now a forestry way and kept for private use. They stopped and surveyed the scene; the other dropped the umbrella, offered a hand, and he, clasping the camera firmly in one hand, drew himself up, balanced, then reached over to the other side. He offered the umbrella to him and then followed suit, both were presently arranged, expectant and a little flushed, now standing on the far side.

The path stretched from their current position, winding a little through the uneven clump of trees, to make its way as far as a bridge, before it dissolved into the distant shred of mist. They gathered themselves and began to walk, their steps light though at first a little unsure, until they became more used to the uneven pace. The banked roadway was cracking and was turning to mud, as the drainage systems on either side faltered as the crush of decayed twigs and discarded leaves, clogged the filter of water. The glen and side of hill were closely becoming blanketed with a fine wet mist which soared in from the crest of the mountain, to shelter on the leeward side. Although their dress was not equipped to deal with soaking weather and although they may have been expected to turn back at the sight of such greyness, they continued and even displayed some sense of enjoyment at the discomfort each was experiencing. The one with the camera, after an initial flourish of framing, had decided to abandon the task temporarily and had half replaced the camera in its zip-up plastic cover. The umbrella-holder had understood the nature of his task and positioned himself to the left of the other, holding the umbrella to parry the rain which was beginning to fall with increasing severity. At least the camera would be dry.

They took to the path with gusto, he finding the line somewhere between the nearside bank and the middle ridge, while the other more or less followed in the wake, content to orchestrate himself around the camera with his umbrella. Suddenly from no clear direction appeared two figures, small at first and not easily distinguishable, but soon the bodies gained shape and there presently arrived two boys. Two young boys, of around ten years of age, drawing closer, then parallel, now swiftly passing, past. Solemn and with sullen eyes they kept their regard apart, but for a short while, perhaps inadvertently their gaze crossed over and fixed on the other mounting the hill. Hidden behind their line of sight was a precision, a passion, a calling which chilled as it touched and made the other two pause. It seemed that they should stop and follow the sight of the two young boys, but it was too late they had been and they had gone and now only a disturbance was left behind. Nothing nakedly visible, indeed not even a faltering step could be discerned during this event but the imprint was there, the unsettling moment had begun. The camera was passed to the other and walking was regained with added vigour.

The other, unused to the mechanical handling of such a device, broke into a watery grin, unconsciously making gargling sounds which were quite, quite evident. With faltering dexterity one hand clasped the stem of the umbrella, leaving the other free to manipulate the camera from its sheath and he moved it quickly to his eye, which glorified, revelled in such a miraculous extension to itself. Lurching, grabbed flailing images blurted by, half opaque, bleached, before the contrast tightened down to a murky blackness. Such untoward joy. Such natural constraint. Is it possible to disconnect each thing from itself and still arrive at a recognisable record? Besides, if done quickly enough, nothing has time to respond or to cover itself over, scared of a snatched soul bleeding dry. Faced each time with the end of trunk, the sweeping low branches skirting the head of fern and bracken, leading away to some far vanishing alleyway of fir, fencing and firebreak. He gesticulated wildly, arching the camera in broad sweeps, swinging, like some gaunt bird of prey in flight escaping the bullet of the hunter. The action brought him round further, still shut off from outside contact, apart from the view through the lens. The concentration was given instead to the trees and their mildewed trunks which imparted a solemnity and independence that, otherwise, was too shaded to be noticed. Caught in these scenes intimately, he merely put foot after foot forward, automatically, without expression.

But the other,

he was locked deep in thought, his way of moving isolating, crisp, a steady manoeuvre of himself against the elements. The day was turning ominous, the rain now cut broad swathes through the grain of the afternoon. His restlessness was deep rooted, ever since he had passed the two boys he had been aware of a more profound, a more stark malaise in his condition. A rock lay in his way and in revenge he kicked at it, catching the lower eye of one of his boots against its sharp side, and ripping his nearside instep as a result. The pain was insatiable, but it was the weight of anger, directed against this by now bloody stone which shook him. If only he could pick up the rock and hurl it, defiantly, to reciprocate the violence with such a true aim, that it would smash whatever the chosen target. He, the renegade and iconoclast: fighting the good fight, ripping down false prophets, the sirens of hate; putting torch to the bigots, the moralists and their kind. And what in its place should be placed but the decency of passion, of commitment to an other: of he and he.

The flapping of his sole became his rejoinder as the path became rougher, narrower he was ascending; the valley lay below, now almost forgotten. His sole gave him a peculiar sensation, realising that it was undone and dragging, made him laugh, in retort, but secretly, inside. There, he felt it again, a draining, a threat of something alien, ugly, giving vent from within. Perhaps it was the culmination of the day, the weather so miserable and the wetness permeating to clog his clothes tightly to his skin, making movement uncomfortable and abrasive. No, this couldn't really be the case, and he shuddered, in spasms, uncontrollably, and was on the verge of dismissing these thoughts from his mind. Then in a sudden, his look took a glaze, weighed by the bitterness of such a sodden day. The mood of the evenings already spent, welled forth from memory. The automatic activities and chores carried out, contrived to dull the mind. How each evening his thoughts festered and multiplied, decimating chasms of grief littered the shining path of sleep. Every night both he and he and others packed into the tigh dubh, huddled around peat fires, supping the broth and listening to the wind skirting the stone walls and bellowing down stone wells. Although in most senses he enjoyed being there, to the denuded hills and the blackened crofts of neglected Dalriada, it also gave him cause for concern. He was beginning to feel that it may have been a mistake, it may have been wiser to have remained elsewhere.

His thoughts receded, he was now approaching the breech of the hill, the path became flatter and less weary with the crest almost upon him. Now he had nearly reached the point where darting mist roared to almost touch his head, like stabbing, jabbing tendrils of motion. Looking back, the precipitous shreds of sheeting rain effectively sanctioned a cordon between himself and what had gone before. The isolation seemed complete, in the haste he had forgotten his companion and in recompense he called out his name. No reply answered his call, his voice echoed chastely from the curve of the hill. Half wanting to quit, half determined to persevere he was caught for some moments, indecisive and forlorn. Then his strength grew, marshalled and propelled itself by means of legs and arms and shortly his pace quickened, he was moving upwards once more. He felt at once feverish, at once chilled, but he was in motion, moving quite apart from any decision within himself.

Oblivious, restless and with his heart beating wildly, he was running, feeling more breathless, more giddy, sicker, wishing he was able to come to rest. What was it that was happening, with this stilted mist hanging, obscuring the view of all but the immediate path ahead. And then he felt as if there were someone nearby, as if there were someone on the summit waiting, waiting to greet him.

The clouds were thickening, tumbling shapes and darker shadings, compressed, threatened, hung over, loomed, waiting for judgement to be called. He ran faster, caught by something both mysterious and awesome, a sharp pain clogged his side, a rapture latent within him bursting forth, an occasional blinding confusion. Events seemed to be slipping away, voices were welling from the inside and were poised to be audible. He was keeping his head pointed firmly downwards, but he could feel a disresonance and his eyes searched over the stencilling shading of rock, scrub and moor. But it was upwards, up to the sky and the heavens, the clouds and rain that his eyes reached and there, lay a blurred outline of saltire, vague and dismembered, random and partially obscured. It was turning, as if alive, pivoting even, testing its shape and form, slowly dissolving to other figures begging recognition. He was transfixed, suddenly stilled, gaping at the rawness of the signs and transformations. Now more clouds were being arranged and for a moment he could swear that a shrouded figure was distinguishable, arm outstretched, pointing, accusing, a lamentation of rage. The other hand clutched tightly to its robe hanging in furls, as if to beat at its hidden heart. Just as it seemed that they may be some sort of communication, the wind grew stronger and all went awry, the sky momentarily clearing, the celestial blue briefly highlighting the monochrome grey.

Then away, he was away; down, down, down, fleeing from the path of fortune, scared and shaking, hurtling through the muddy clay pools and scarcely pausing for breath. A weight bore down on him, but he was in flight, at once free, apart from the vision and at once taken, beholden, caught by the etched crossing of the clouds, sparkling, stalking across the sky. The wind was behind as he moved, the mist more noticeable as the trail wound downwards, the line of escarpment was broken by the ploughed furrows of tender young lain trees. Quickly now, he was splashing through the congregation of rippling puddles, the rain washing across its surface. He was trying not to reason, trying to ignore the anguish of pained muscles, threatening cramp and the pull of sodden clothes. There, he was now firmly descending, the rim of the path came into view, as far as the bridge across the initial stream.

His pace didn't slacken, but now he had a reference point, he could see exactly how far needed to be covered and he felt hopeful. Presently he was there, he had arrived at the wooden planks and the criss-crossed supports of the bridge. The other was now noticeable, on the far bank, questioning in his regard as the approach drew nearer. Pausing mid-way he looked down and could notice that between the cracks of the wood and the holes of the ferrous nails, lay the stream, flowing as a solid conjecture, broken rarely by the spinning vortex of wheeling, eddy and ripple.

He hung to the rail and let the top part of his body curl over the banister and his dangling head could catch the full undistracted view of the dark, clear mass, seething below. The cool distilled surface spread by, reflecting and on occasion giving access to the stores of its depth. Broken litter, discarded utensils, a large worn-out rubber tyre lay weighted to the smooth bank, layers of debris accumulating from the rubbish of an abandoned generation. And yet if he were to look further afield, if he followed the curve of the river as far as he was able to see, he knew that in turn, it would run smoothly into the sea.

Conversation With Carla

Carla was born in Mozambique, emigrated to Rhodesia, married a man from Edinburgh, came back to Britain to live in Surrey for two years, then moved to her present location in a small town outside Edinburgh.

'D', my husband, didn't accept me loving another girl when I told him I was a lesbian, but after a while he accepted me as Carla — 100 per cent. In fact, he was the one who encouraged me to go down to the Lesbian and Gay Centre in Edinburgh. He walked me to the door with the kids in tow and said that we could all have a look inside, the kids as well, but even though I was shaking from head to toe, I said eventually, after we walked past the place at least four times, if I was going to do this I might as well do it on my own.

That wasn't enough. Slowly I was coming out but I wasn't really aware of it. I was terrified of anyone finding out, especially since the girl I had met stays in the same place as me, very close by. My husband knew but he wouldn't tell, and the whole situation became like something out of *Dallas* or *Dynasty*. I was in a situation where I couldn't tell anyone.

Eventually a rumour began to go around that I was having an affair with one of my friends' husband. I went to visit her just for a coffee or something, and she started saying, after a lot of stuttering, that I was having an affair with her husband.

I thought, to hell with this, I mean, I could hardly believe it! And I couldn't reassure her enough, more than saying 'No, I have never had an affair with your husband'. But she still wasn't convinced, so I said, listen, I'll tell you something, if it was between you and your husband, if I was going to have an affair with one of you, it would be you! At that she automatically covered her legs and said 'What!?' And then, after the initial shock, she said, 'Really?' I nodded and she burst out laughing. Once I had said that I found it a lot easier to speak to her.

Meantime I met somebody who was new in my circle of friends here, who I no longer see but she was very open-minded. She spoke quite easily about her feelings and she is totally man crazy. And she couldn't understand why I didn't have a man. It would come up in the conversation all the time, 'So you've been separated from your husband and you have no boyfriends?' — No — 'Aren't you interested in having boyfriends?' — No — Because she was man-mad she couldn't understand why I wasn't. Eventually she just asked one night, 'Are you gay?' and I said I was. And it was a lot easier than the first time. She asked me if any of my other friends knew, which they didn't, and she encouraged me to tell them, saying that if she was the last one in the circle then all the others should know. She was prepared to come to Edinburgh with me again, and even go to gay discos with me to keep me company. It was then that I decided to tell each woman in my own time, taking each one in turn — I couldn't tell them all at once.

It was important to me that I did tell them individually because on their own I felt I could get their attention and having to explain why I felt like this, but more than that, I wanted them to fully understand that all of a sudden I wasn't a lesbian whose name was Carla — I was still Carla, except that I just had different feelings. For me it was important that one didn't overrule the other. It would be easy to say that woman is a lesbian and then forget the personality. Even a thief or a drunk has feelings . . . it's all labels. I wanted my friends to know me better than they had before. It's quite easy, even when you know a person, to let this label cover you up.

One of my friends ('I') who just stays a couple of doors up from me has got a very different attitude towards sex. She's open-minded, and a single parent: maybe that has something to do with it and with me not having a husband it made it easier for her to come in and see me sometimes. But she's a nutcase! She's been married, got two kids — how on earth she gave birth to those two children, is beyond me, how on earth she made it is beyond me. The minute you mention the word 'sex' she falls asleep. She's twenty-nine and on the other hand I have another friend who is in her forties ('A') and when those two are together it's difficult to keep one awake. If you don't talk about sex one falls asleep, and if you do, the other falls asleep. So I was always in the middle trying to keep the conversation going.

So, I chose 'I' to tell next. I couldn't get round to saying what I wanted to. I kept on saying, 'I want to tell you something.' It wasn't her reaction that I was wary of, it's just that she doesn't even know how she made her children so how was she going to understand what I was trying to tell her! Anyway, she was very tired and said that if I didn't tell her she was going to go to sleep. Eventually she did fall asleep and at about three o'clock in the morning I woke her up. 'I've got to tell you.' 'Right, I'll help you — you're having an affair with a man' — I said no; 'you're having an affair with the lollipop lady' — nearly there; 'you're going to prison for something or other' — no; 'you're having an affair with the lollipop lady' — well not quite the lollipop lady but a lady all the same. She said, 'For Pete's sake is that all, can I get some sleep now?' And that was her reaction.

One of 'I's kids came up to me not long after and said, 'You're a lemon'. Well, I'd never heard this expression before and 'I' explained to me that it was another word meaning 'lesbian'. We all had a good laugh about this because there was no longer this pressure on me. If we went out, they used to say 'we need to get you a boyfriend' and I'd say yeah. And then all of a sudden it was 'do you think she's nice, come on, is that your type we've got to find someone for you'.

Another friend, 'E', reacted in a different way when I told her. She said that she knew about it and that she had known for quite a while. I asked her how she knew and she just said that she always thought that it was obvious. So I had told each of my friends apart from one.

'A' was the only one to give me criticism. I knew I had to encounter someone like that. I was terrified of telling her. I felt uneasy about telling the other girls but I knew that 'A' would take it very differently from them. I got 'A' on her own and I told her and she said that she now understands an awful lot of things. She always used to ask my opinions of things and that now a lot of my answers made sense. She said that she needed time to think about what I had told her. So I gave her time. I mean, I've needed four years to get to this point so she could have all the time in the world as far as I was concerned. So she went away and I never pressurised her and I told the other girls not to ask questions or anything, just to leave her. She used to pass my window for many weeks after that and not come in. And if she did come in she always made sure that she had somebody else with her.

Then one day she came on her own and said right out, 'You know something, you can be whatever you are but I still like you.' 'A' was what I needed the most, she gave me criticism and took what I had said to her seriously.

'A' and the other girls used to come round to the house asking me to do their hair or their eyebrows. Now there is only one way I can do eyebrows, and that's if the person lies on my lap. I said to one of them that if I wanted to take advantage of them it would be then. But just because I'm a lesbian didn't mean to say that I'm going to pounce on every woman that I meet. And eventually they understood that, so now I can kiss them, hug them and be open with them. 'A' comes round quite a lot to get her eyebrows done and she was quite hurt when she found out that she wasn't my type — 'what's the matter with me?'

I think I've had it easy but it was hard at the time. I treasure my friendships, even the basic kinds of relationship. They are all individuals to me, there's something about each of them that I love.

transcribed by Toni Davidson, December 1988

Spring 1971

Simon Taylor

It was a beautiful spring. I spent it in a heavily gardened suburb of Hamburg called Eissendorf. I lived with an elderly lady in a little thatched cottage which looked like something out of *Hansel and Gretel.* It stood right at the edge of the woods, in a huge garden full of trees which towered high above the roof. It was like living on the bottom of a pond. The air was green water, and the trees were some great submarine growths slowly swaying in the sluggish currents. And I remember a great orange moon floating on warm, richly scented evenings.

10th May 1971

I have never experienced the spring like this before, with such force, such awareness, such joy. My being is released from its confines by the overpowering perfume, the glossy greens of the new-born leaves, the fragrance of new life. It is absorbed, intoxicated, into the beckoning sea of light and warmth.

Suburb town of village slumbers
  nightly no one stirs;
Chimney-cradles moon of amber
  in amongst tired stars.
Dream-like mist lies down-like over,
  death-pale street-lights pour light over
  rooves of houses housing dreamers
  dreaming sweetly far from where they are.

It was the sort of time and place where poems flourished along with the vegetation. There are many from that spring in Eissendorf.

For example *The Song of the Wood Spirit*

Ever since the trees cast their shadows
  long across the land at sunset;
ever since leaves broke the sun's rays
  into a thousand flakes of light,
I have been there,
in the silent glade,
in the hollow of shadows,
in the leaves as they whisper beneath the wind,
at dawn, when the space between the trees is
  filled
  with milky mist and bird-song,
I am there. . . .

Then came May 13th. I regard that day as determining the direction of my life for the next two years at least. As the date itself might suggest, it was amongst the worst directions it could have gone.

I am writing a lot in my diary in mid and late May,

but nowhere do I make any direct mention of the 13th. However, on the 13th I wrote a letter to my parents, which I had absolutely no intention of sending. This is what it said:

Today I experienced a most interesting, extraordinary and traumatic hour and a half. I had my soul, past and present, taken apart by a psychiatrist.

Why did I think it necessary to take such drastic measures? To answer that I must now talk about that dark, unmentionable and secret thing called sex. And why do I feel so uncomfortable in talking about such a natural, beautiful thing to my own parents, to the lovers I owe my existence to? Perhaps what I'm about to say has something to do with the answer to that question, so I'll come to the point as briefly as possible. You see, I've always been firmly convinced that I was homosexual. There were reasons enough for that dreadful thought. I think it would be best now to tell you what happened this afternoon.

I can't remember everything exactly — there are already large gaps in the tying in of facts and diagnosis. All I can say is that at the time everything fitted together perfectly into so glaringly obvious a pattern that I was amazed I had never seen it before. Actually the truth, beautiful in its simplicity, is far kinder to everybody concerned than I had ever hoped.

The first man I ever saw and knew was, of course, my father. And my father has only one leg. This fact was in my consciousness, and unconscious, long before I could understand the explanation for this state of affairs. At the very genesis of all feeling and awareness one thought held sway which should not really have been there at all: that to be grown-up, to be a man, meant losing a great part of me. The result of this thought was fear, fear that sometime in my future life I, too, would lose a part of me. And my reaction to this fear, my way of combating it, was to escape into a world of no fear, a world where there were complete men, good-looking, strong, active, a world of erotic fearlessness where the whole man had free rein, the whole man whom I was convinced I would not or could not become. I eroticised my fear in order to live with it.

The erotic side of it all developed, of course, rapidly and by itself, gathering more and more momentum, like a stone rolling down a hill.

There the letter breaks off, and I find no other reference to this 'most interesting, extraordinary and traumatic' event until summer 1976, five years later, when I was asked to write a summary of my coming out. There I described my brief encounter with psychiatry as follows:

I compensated this fear, which I talk about in the letter (unsent) to my parents, in two ways: (1) by eroticising dangerous situations. This is what I was supposedly doing in my earliest remembered erotic dream, when I was about five. In this dream I was standing by a river watching a man in swimming trunks caught in the downward surge of a waterfall or weir. He was being turned over and over by the rush of water. I, as an observer, was filled with very strong erotic feelings which I can still clearly remember. Also from a very early age I used to have erotic fantasies about ships in storms or ships sinking. I would often masturbate for upwards of quarter of an hour to these fantasies.

(2) by focusing my eroticism on the object of my unnatural fear: my body and the bodies of other men. In myself and other men I was looking for what I was deeply afraid of losing — my wholeness as a man.

The psychiatrist's theory was that I simply had to come to realise that becoming a 'complete man' (which presumably included being heterosexual) would not involve any risk to life or, more importantly, limb, that I was a 'complete man'. All I had to do was to gain confidence in that fact, and abracadabra I would become 'normal'. Unfortunately in 1971 I was not protected from that most pernicious word by those inverted commas.

I remember the psychiatrist as quite a young man with a quiet, gentle manner. Dr Meuthen was his name. He had lived for a time in England, and we discussed whether to conduct the session in English or German. We decided on German. My most vivid recollection is a gesture he made when getting me to describe my fiancée. 'Is she?' he asked, and with a kind of conspiratorial look he drew in the air with both hands the figure of eight — representing the standard desirable female shape.

I had only one session with him. He sent me away with the assurance that I was not homosexual, and a grasp of the breathtaking logic of my sexual development was all I needed to gain the confidence to become a red-blooded, penis-toting, figure-of-eight-female-body-screwing heterosexual man. So he sent me away with exactly that assurance that I was longing to hear. The monster had been named and tamed and destroyed all in an afternoon. He said he had never come across a clearer, more perfect case, with so many vital details so well remembered.

I was over the moon. I was beside myself with joy and excitement. I was heterosexual.

But by the summer I am writing a homosexual love-story which I preface with the following remark:

> There is the thought that this story might fulfil me as nothing ever has done in all my life previous to this. I am frightened of the god called fantasy.
>
> Five days after my 'conversion' to heterosexuality in May my fiancée, Beate. and I went to Berlin.

There I became horribly fascinated by the place, the 'sick child' of Germany, with its decay, its division, its degradation. It was my first real encounter with the ugly face of politics and some of the harsh realities of the world 'outside'. I was shocked and fascinated enough to turn my attention, briefly, from the nastiness within to the nastiness without.

When we got back from Berlin we spent a week out in the country at Beate's parents' weekend cottage. We were on our own, it was warm, there were beautiful woods all around. Romance blossomed once again, this time, I was convinced, founded on Truth. Indeed my memories of that time are happy — some of the very few. I was no longer responsible for the pretending, the elaborate play-acting. This responsibility had been taken over by the medical and scientific establishment, as represented by Dr Meuthen. I was clean. I was a real man. And for a few weeks I was happy.

When did the doubts begin to stir? When did Dr Meuthen's story begin to ring hollow?

It is impossible now to say. But I do know that by midsummer I had started to write a love-story. It was about a man, who, while eating out with his wife one evening, falls in love with a man he sees in the restaurant. I never got beyond the moment he sets eyes on him, which happens at the top of the second page. The rest of the page is blank.

Rab's Story

A'M CRYIT RAB, an A win on a muckle fairmtoun i Fife. A'll be twinty year auld come Januar neist, eichteen hunnert an ninety.

A hae lang kent A wis no a lassie's man. A'm young, swank and swack, sae it's no that A cannae get yin; they're aye blinkin at me. But aa A dae is eisen; a bonnie young plooman wi a boozy warklum has aye ruggit me mair nor ony lassie.

Ye micht think it'd be nae mowse fur a cheil the likes o me, awaa oot i the kintra. Weel, ye'll be fair dumfoonert; A've no bin oot o the aumry lang, but oot A am, an A hae a man fur a marrow an aa. An A'm ettlin tae tell ye hoo it aa come aboot.

Aa the cheils whaa arenae mairrit bide thegither i the bothy, a muckle biggin, like tae a byre wiooten the kye. A yaist tae lig i ma bed ilka nicht watchin the cheils pitting aff thir duds an thinkin ma graith wud breenge thru ma bed-plyde. There wis ane lad i particlar. Jock he wis cryit. On warm nichts he'd pit aff aa his claes an sleep bare-scuddie. Fegs, but he wis a braw swankie.

He wis aboot ages wi me. He wis nairrie-bukit, wi braid shooders, strang airms an theis, a muckle cullage, an a wee, harth towdy. He had a baird on him as gowden as the bere at the hairst; he wis ferntickled, wi a sonsy face an bonnie blue een.

Fae the time he come tae oor fairmtoun — that'll be twaa year noo come Michaelmas — he waled the bed neist tae mines, an ma nichts wur fu o seilfu dreams o him. He wis aye freenly, an affen at nicht we wud lig bletherin i oor beds till the ither cheils gollered oot til us tae hud oor wheesht.

A'd ne'er telt onybody afore aboot ma eisenin. O course A'd had a rowth mowse wi ither hauflins whan A wis a hauflin masel; i the wids, breeks doon, pegos oot, splairgin glit aa owr the grun. Syne whan we got a wee bittie aulder the ithers aa seemed tae want tae gan wi lassies. They telt me A wis fremmit cos A still wantit tae play wi the laddies.

Swith A lernt tae tak ma ain rede aboot it aa, an thocht thon wud aye be the wey o it. It wisnae eith, an whan Jock come tae the bothy, A thocht A'd rin wudd.

Sae Jock an masel, we'd blether aboot aathin. Whiles we talked aboot lassies, but A didnae hae muckle tae sey on the subjek, nor did Jock, fur that maitter. Whit a chynge fae the ither young cheils, aye yabblin aboot them! But A ne'er telt Jock aboot ma dreams o him, an A ne'er dreamt A wud.

Onywey, ane dey aboot sax month efter Jock come tae the fairm A wis caain the coos tae the hamefield tae be mowed by the bu. It wis a warm spring dey an the coos wur eisenin, an they wurnae the anely yins!

Jock wis owrby delvin a wee bit grun fur Mr Watt the fairmer. He had pit aff his sark, an his braw boss wis weet wi sweit an his curple wis fechtin oot his ticht breeks whan he lootit. It wis a sicht fur sair een, an ma een wur gey sair, an no jist ma een.

It wisnae lang afore the bu wi his muckle pillie wis bangin awaa at the coos, an whit wi Jock on the ane side an aa thon by-job on the ither, ma ain pillie wis hovit fit tae birst ma ballup.

Jock cryit oot canty-like, 'Hoo ye daein, Rab?'

'Nae bad. A'm jist steekin the yett afore A tine ony coos.'

'A dinnae think ony o they ull be wantin oot the noo. They've got better things tae dae, dae ye no think?' An he lauched an pit doon his spade gey quick. 'A'll come wi ye,' he said, 'ye micht need a haun.'

Need a haun tae steek a yett? A thocht tae masel. Whit's he haiverin aboot?

A'd done steekin the yett afore he got tae me. A wis leant there, watchin the coos being mowit. He comes up ahint me and pit his twaa hauns on the yett, ane on the yin side o me, ane on the ither. Ma hairt wis duntin wi sic a feck that the yett wis shooglin i ma hauns.

Jock's moo wis richt by ma lug. He sooghed intae it:

'Ilk yaul-cuted heifer, roon thee playin,
I merriment tossin her glaikit heid,
Beneath thy wame licks doon thy boozy lisk,
An rubs thy courage-bag, noo toom's a whussle.'

'Whaur did ye lere thon?' A speirt, ma heid stairtin tae burl.

'Och, A dinnae ken. A jaloos ma faither yaist tae jaw it whan the kye wur at it, or aiblins whan his bandileers wur yukin. Ye ken, Rab, A wud fair like tae lick *yer* lisk an toom *yer* courage-bag, so A wud.'

'Whit?' A speirt i the mirliegoes.

'Dinnae think,' quo he, 'that A huvnae seen ye blinkin at me like tae an eisenin coo syne A come tae the fairm — or an eisenin bu, mair like.'

He wis richt ahint me, an A cid feel his hovit warklum dunting thru his ballup agin ma dowp.

'No here,' A peched. A wis flegged we micht be seen.

'Dinnae fash yersel, ma loon,' quo he. Syne as croose as ye like he seys, 'Wull ye gan tae Clatto Wid wi me? A'll see ye efter crowdie-time ahint the cavie.' He mowpit ma lug an wis awaa back tae the delvin afore A cid sey houghmagandie.

Thon nicht A cidnae get ma tea doon me. Ma wame wis sweellin, an A wis gey near bokin.

'Whit's wrang wi ye?' speirt Meg the ktichie deem. 'Ye've scarce etten a nip. It maun be a lassie. Whaa is she, eh?'

Ma face riddened like it wis alowe. Meg gaffit, 'Tak a keek at the loon!' she skreiched. 'He's as reid as a beetruit.'

Aa the lassies an cheils wis lauchin noo, an speirin daft-like things like 'Whit's she cryit?' an 'Are ye seein her the nicht?'

'Awaa tae Freuchie an fry mice, the lot o ye!' A munged, an wis oot thon kitchie i a glent.

It wis guid tae be oot i the warm saucht o the gloamin an awaa fae aa thon flyran. A gaed tae the cavie. Nae Jock. Ma hairt fair sunk.

A gey near shat masel whan a vyce ahint me said, 'Wull ye tak a turn wi me, laddie?'

A burled roon. There wis Jock, swack an croose.

'Aye, that A wull,' A seys, an we tuik the gate tae Clatto Wid.

The Wid wis a fair bittie up the brae. Man, but it wis bonnie, wi the knowes happit i yellie whin, the trees jist shawin thir sprush-new green, an the cloods aa reid fae the deyset. The lift wis warm and filt wi the wheep o the peesies an the threepin o the corbies i the craw-widdie.

We wur i the Wid noo, whaur it wis mirk an caum an dern.

'Dinnae gan ony faurer,' Jock said, pittin his haun on ma shooder. A turned roon an he ruggit me tae him an preed ma moo. Ma airms gaed roon his boss.

'Tak yer claes aff!' he sooghed, an stairtit ruggin aff ma sark an ma simmit. I a glent we wur bare-scuddie the baith o us. Fegs but it wis braw tae fin his nakit buke agin mines, an his biggened warklum hot an gowpin on ma wame.

He duntit me doon lithe-like ontae a bittie gress. His moo an his hauns wur aa owr me, ma face, ma hause, ma boss, ma whang. A grained, 'Caa canny, else ye'll be slorpin glit.'

He lauched an preed ma moo. 'Dinnae fash yersel aboot thon, laddie, A've no had ma brose the dey.'

'Awaa wi ye, ye scunnersome loon!' A cryit.

A mowpit his paps, an ma hauns wur dautin his harth towdy an his ticht courage-bag. Syne A mowpit an sookit faurer doon, doon tae his wame an faurer yet, tae his whappin warklum, aa sauty, weet an steive. Swith he ruggit ma hale buke roon an stairtit sookin ma bandileers an in atween ma dock.

'A'm gaun tae splairge,' A grained, an toomed ma culls intae his moo, wuntlin an lauchin, syne A fell back forfochten.

He didnae slorp ma glit. Insteid he spat it oot ontae his

haun, burled me owr ontae ma wame an slaiked ma dowp an his graith wi a plowter o ma glit an his slaver.

'A want tae thirl ye, Rab,' he sooghed. 'Wull ye thole me?'

Ma rumple-fyke wis muckle yet, an A heistit ma hurdies a wee tae sey aye.

He had me ticht i his airms, an A cid feel his warm pechs i ma lug, an his warm pego reengin deep ben. Fegs, but it wis braw! Efter a whilie he tuik ma breengin mowdiewart i his wicht neive an friggit me wi birr.

Syne his hale buke wuntled widd-like an he near deaved me wi a goller as he tooomed hissel intae me. Weel, thon did me, an A jauped ma glit aa owr his haun an the gress an the spinkies forby.

We liggit lang no steirin a thow. Jock's pego hovit an ben me yet. Efter a whilie Jock speirt douce-like, 'Are ye aaricht, ma mannie?'

'A cannae mind feelin better,' A sooghed. 'But A'm a pickle cauld gettin.'

He ruggit hissel oot o me an A grained wi the pleeshur an the wae o it. We pit on oor duds an oor bits, preeing an hausin. Jock wis staunin there saw brawly, A had tae pu a spinkie an pit it ahint his lug.

'Whaa's the heich-skeich loon noo?' he keckled, an preed ma lips.

It wis gey mirk by noo, an a drow wis creepin thru the wid. We tuik the gate hamewith.

'Can we dae thon again belyve?' Jock speirt wi a skinkle i his ee.

'Can we no!' A says, as we come oot o Clatto Wid an lookit oot owr the mirknin knowes.

Mar A Thubhairt A'Chrè Ris A'Chriadhadair

Christopher Whyte

Is aithne dhomh do làmhan
an sùbailteachd an ciùine
thomhais mi gach miar dhiubh
fhaide leud a thri-fhillteachd
cruinnead eugsamhail nan roinn
caochanan gach luirge
cruadal d'òrdaig dhanarra
a h-ainneart nach gabh faothachadh.

Tha eagal orm roimh dhealbhadh:
carson nach deach mo dhearmad
gu sultmhor dràbach somalta
an teàrmann na talmhainn
'nam làthaich liath-ghlais fhuar-shiltich
a' deoghal cìoch mo mhàthar truim
caillt' an loch-bhlèin garbh-shlios
an neo-chumadh gam shàsachadh?

Is borb dian gun trocair thu
dhlùthaich thu orm gun fhaireachadh
cha toir mi dhuit na dh'iarradh tu
is cealgach faoin do dhòchasan
's tu smaoineachadh ri cumadh fiùghail

What The Clay Said To The Potter

Christopher Whyte

I know your hands
their suppleness their repose
the span of each finger
its length breadth and triplicity
the varying roundness of each joint
the eddy of each fingertip
the compulsion of your forceful thumb
its unrelenting violence.

I am afraid of taking shape:
couldn't I have been left alone
dripping, plump, complacent
the ground my sanctuary
a quagmire, oozing, cold, grey-green
sucking my heavy mother's breast
lost in the groin of some rough hill
satisfied with shapelessness?

You're savage, impulsive, pitiless
you came up on me without warning
I'm not going to give you what you want
you're kidding yourself if you think that you
can extract any kind of worthwhile

a tharraing às bho fhrionasachd
ghabh thu ort gu ladarna
comh-èigneachadh ri pearsantachd.

Ach thionndaidh thu mi
        ann an leabaidh do làmhan
d'fhaigse a'leaghadh
        mo thiughaid raig

aig suathadh do bhlàiths
        thòisich mo ghluasad
chaidh m'fhiosrachadh
        aig t'anail gun fhois.

A chruthadair neo-ghlic
        's tu struidheil de ghibhtean
co às a fhuair thu
        uibhir de ghaol

a sgapadh gun chiall
        a chaitheamh neo-chùramach
mise gam bheartachadh
        tusa gun lùghachadh?

Is e friamh mo dhìlse
        do mhiann do-shàsaicht'
truimead do làmhan
        air rèidheachd mo chrè

mise gad fhreagairt
        an iomadach cruitheachd
aighear ar cleasa
        comh-chòrdadh ar rùin.

form from my resistance.
You set out ill-advisedly
to force me into personality.

But you turned me
      in the bed of your hands
your closeness melting
      my stubborn mass

caressing your warmth
      I started to move
your restless breathing
      made me conscious.

Foolish creator
      squandering gifts
where did you get
      this kind of love

to scatter recklessly
      to use undauntedly
making me richer
      while you got no poorer?

What makes me so faithful
      is your endless desire
the weight of your hands
      on my ready clay

as I talk back
      in multiple forms
ecstatic play
      and single intent.

An Coisreagadh

Christopher Whyte

Thàinig dithis gu dorsan an teampuill
an aodach duslachail air an sracadh
le cruadalachd nan sràidean Greugach.
Cha do leugh an dorsair 'nan sùilean
ach sgìos bhalbh luchd-turuis
bodach is balach gun bhruidhinn le chèile
is a-rèir laghannan an àite
thugadh dhaibh biadh is aoigheachd.
Dh'amhairc e orra gu fidreachail
am bodach a' glàmadh gu mi-mhodhail
a chuid peasraich is arain, agus am balach
a' frithealadh air gu dìcheallach,
a' dearmad a bhìdh fhèin, gun fhacal
aithneachaidh no tainge fhaighinn bho 'mhaighstir.
Shuidhich e iad an àite suarach
air beulaibh staidhrichean nan seilear
fad bho sheòmar coisrigte nan deas-ghnàth
oir bha iad beagan breuntach on t-seachran.
Dh'fhalbh an dorsair leis a' chrùisgean
is dh'fhàg e iad fo dhorchadas nan stuagh.

Cha d'fhuair am balach cadal, no faodaidh gun d'fhuair;
ach beagan an dèidh sin chuala e guth

Consecration

Christopher Whyte

Two came to the temple doors
their clothing torn and dusty
from the harshness of the Greek roads.
In their eyes the porter read only
the dumb exhaustion of travellers
an old man and a boy who exchanged no words
and according to the laws of the place
they were given food and lodging.
He watched them with interest
as the old man ill-manneredly
gulped down his share of beans and bread
while the boy waited on him attentively
forgetting his own food, and receiving
neither thanks nor acknowledgement from his master.
They were assigned a lowly place
in front of the stairs to the cellar
far from the room reserved for sacred rites
(they stank a little from their wandering).
The porter took the lamp away with him
and left them in the darkness of the vaults.

The boy could get no sleep, or maybe he did,
but soon after he heard a voice,

cha b'urrainn dha tuigsinn am b'e
guth boireannaich no fir a bh'ann
'ga thàladh cho geasach ciùin
gun do dh'èirich e, is do lean e ris
a' faicinn roimhe seòrsa cumadh lainnireach
no iasg lasrach a-measg uisgeachan
sgàileach trannsaichean an teampuill.
Dh'fhàs an guth 'na cheòl neo-cheannsaichte
is mhothaich e mar a leaghadh dorsan
de dharaich len glasan troma
roimh dhraoidheachd a' chumaidh, is esan fhèin
ri dannsaireachd a-nist, is gann gum beanadh
a chasan ris an làr. Ràinig iad
àrd-sheòmair an àite, is chunnaic e
gu robh na ballachan air an dealbhadh
le fir is boireannaich a bha aoibhneach 'nan luime
a' coinneachadh a chèile fo làn-bhlàth
nan geug, is ainmhidhean a' nochdadh
an-dràsd 's a-rithist bho dhiamhaireachd nam preas.
Bha cuilbh an t-seòmair a' coimhead air,
ag èigheachd ris 'nan cànan clachach
a' foillseachadh dha rùintean
a bha e eòlach orra a cheana
an àiteigin caillte ann an doimhn' a spioraid.
Bha 'fhuil a' bualadh le ruithim an togalaich uile
is chunnaic e gun robh a' chiad lasair
air fàs lìonmhor, is mìle teintean
ri dannsaireachd os cionn na h-altair.
Tholl riomball nan teine a chrè fhèin
is thòisich e ann an gàirdeachas làn cràidh
air seinn le guth coigreach nach do dh'aithnich e.

whether a man's or a woman's he could not tell,
summoning him so magically, gently
that he got up, and followed it,
seeing a sort of glinting shape in front of him,
a fish of flame in the shadowy
waters of the temple corridors.
The voice swelled to a reckless music
and he observed how the oaken doors
with their heavy locks, melted before
the enchanting shape, and he himself
was dancing now, his feet scarcely
touching the floor. They reached
the chief room of the place, and he saw
that the walls were painted with
men and women joyous in nakedness
coming together under the full blossom
of trees, and animals peering here and there
out from the secrecy of bushes.
The pillars of the chamber looked on him,
calling to him in their stone language
revealing mysteries to him
he already knew, somewhere in
a hidden place deep in his spirit.
His blood was beating with the rhythm of the whole building
and he saw that the first flame
had multiplied, and a thousand fires
were dancing above the altar.
The circle of fire pierced his flesh
and in a laughter full of pain he started
singing in a strange voice he did not recognise.

Fhuaradh lomnochd 'sa mhadainn e
neo-fhiosrach, ach beò, is bha na sagartan
ri deasbaireachd mun dìoghaltas
a fhreagradh ri fear a bhrùth a-steach
don àite-naomh, ach chuir an t-Ard-dhruidh
na thosd iad, oir chunnaic e
air sgòrnan a' bhalaich an comharradh
a dh'fhàgas an dia air an fheadhainn a thaghas e
is nach fhaod an ciùrradh.

Sin am bruadar a bh'aig a' bhàird 'na òige
's a dh'innis e dhuinn 'sna làithean roimh a bhàs
nuair a bha e feuchainn ri a bheatha
a shoilleireachadh s a cheartachadh.

They found him naked in the morning,
senseless, but living, and the priests
set to disputing what kind of punishment
was fitting for one who had profaned
the sacred place, but the high priest
put them to silence, for he had seen
on the boy's neck the sign the god
leaves on those he has chosen, and whom
it is forbidden to harm.

This is the dream the poet had in his youth
and told to us in the days before he died
when he was striving to explain
and justify the kind of life he'd led.

Biorhythms

Helen

Biorhythms
At a low ebb
Play pure Hell
With your emotions
Childish thoughts
Passing through your mind;
No stopping them.
Upset, hurt
For no fathomable reason.
Prior knowledge of low ebbs
Would be of
Advantage
Provide the ability
To avoid
Susceptible situations.
Being silly
I know
Twenty-four hours
So far.
How much longer?
Not like me.
Not usual.
Don't like it.

Feel stupid.
Feel pleased
at small gestures of affection
I'm remembered.
Feel something's wrong;
Don't know what . . .
Probably imagination
On a low ebb
Pure Hell
Bring back the high
Biorhythms.
Far preferable.
Don't like these feelings
Childish stupidity
Susceptability
Pub emptying now
No time to talk
You've got to go.

The Longest Journey

TOMMY BARCLAY

THE LONGEST JOURNEY, so they say, begins with one step. And that first step, according to similar smartarses, is the hardest. But you all know that, don't you? So at work you're one of the lads. A poofter-joke in the canteen, and your laugh is as raucous as the next guy's. It's easier that way, isn't it? Of course it is — much simpler. What's your gayness got to do with them, anyway? Whose bloody life is it, eh? There you are, then. Problem solved. Problem? What problem?

What the hell, at weekends you can shine, can't you? Weekends you can let the real you off the leash for a frolic or two. Blossom a bit. And why not? You work hard all week, you're entitled to a boogie now and then. So what if it is somewhere well out of the way of your day-to-day life, you're paying, aren't you? Well then. But what if — well, what if you're out on the floor at some gay club, thrusting your valuables at all and sundry, and you spot — or (CALAMITY!) are spotted by — some workmates who are injecting a buzz of decadence into their boring night out by visiting a queer disco — what then?

It is now, at the instant of eye-to-eye contact, that considerations of the employment prospects in Australia will cross your mind, as will whether God will, in His infinite mercy, cause a Black Hole to appear on the dance-floor, immediately beneath your feet for preference. For what you decide to do now will influence whether or not you turn up for work — and what your likely reception will be if you do.

Your options, let's be honest, are few. You can vanish, fleet as the wind, and contrive to lock yourself in the bog. Always providing you can convince the inevitable occupants of the urgency of your claim to their little corner of heaven. You can clutch at your forehead, sway dramatically, and with wide haunted eyes, cry, 'Where am I . . .?' before weaving an unsteady path out into the night. You can clasp the arm of the nearest gawping workmate and express your tearful relief, saying, 'Thank God you've arrived, chaps, I'm being held prisoner!' Or you can calmly wink your acknowledgement of their presence, encourage your partner to favour them with a cheery salute, and continue gettin' down to it.

Which is it to be, huh? Let us assume for the sake of argument that you are not Joan Crawford. Right? So that last option is favourite, right? The casual wink from you, the cheery salute from your buddy, the you-rascal-you smiles of recognition from your workmates. Now isn't this a more civilised way to go about things? Doesn't this give you a little glow? No? Well, maybe you're right. Maybe there's no good reason why you should give a bucket of warm sick about what your workmates think or don't think about you. Maybe your greeting should be a glacial grin and a V-sign. But, well, call me a sentimental old toerag if you must, I figure the more straight (you should pardon the expression) I am with people, the straighter they'll be with me. Think you can handle it? Few do. Think they can handle it, that is. But I'm here to tell you that you'll be surprised. You'll be very surprised. Luckily you will already possess something which every gay has, thanks to our enforced lifestyle, to a greater or lesser degree — the ability to think on your feet.

And talking about feet brings us back to the first step. Where do you start? With your own sweet self; that's where. You've got to get it in your mind that, somehow, you'll drop the fact that you're gay-and-happy-to-be-gay into the general pool of conversation at work. To see how the ripples form. No vulgarity, no cheapo campery, no liberated groping of the nearest thigh. Just mention it and move on to the weather, football, the SDP and whether it will turn political, anything. See, what causes more rumour, innuendo, and downright badmouthing, is doubt. Remove the doubt, and they're knackered. Remove the doubt, and you're saying (with quiet dignity), '. . . So . . .?'

Great, you say . . . I stand there being quietly dignified while some cro-magnon piles on the ridicule? My eyes are respectfully downcast while this paunch on legs breaks his wrist, blows a kiss, and sashays off to the tea-machine? Yes. And no. A little craft is required here, a soupcon of guile. And just a modicum of elegant shafting. You may turn to others in the company — for rest assured they'll be watching you — and deadpan them with something like, '. . . and as well as that . . .' (indicating the departing cretin) '. . . I also screw boy scouts, do embroidery, and carry a handbag. As you can all see . . .'

You may not get a standing ovation, but applause you don't need. The ice will be well and truly broken. Suspicions will have been confirmed, but more, they will have effectively have been scuttled by your heavily ironic litany of clichés. I don't say — and don't you believe — that henceforth you will be transformed in their eyes into a Hero of the Sexual Revolution, but what you have done will be of lasting value, not least to yourself. Believe it or not, and I didn't before I came out at work, it is possible to change the people around you, just by honestly being who you are.

It sounds smug and priggish, but the change all round, myself included, is, I believe, for the better. Canteen or smokeroom jokes are no longer quite so clodhoppingly crude, blatant sexism wobbles a bit, with a challenge to macho sexuality sitting right there smiling an arch you-don't-say smile. Now and again, of course, you have to deal with the awkward moments, like someone reading aloud from a Sunday paper the 'sordid story of perverted vice' which has obviously been concocted over a few jars by a hack hounded by deadline. When that happens, you simply ask the reader to carry on to the next shock-horror exclusive, and the next, and the next, and so on, until the point is driven home.

So much for a few of the perils — what are the pleasures? Ah, they are all yours, every day. The knowledge that you are yourself, and the world may like it or loathe it, but here you are. The knowledge that the friends you now have — and some will drift away, sad to say — are friends indeed. The abandonment of pretence — that relief will astound you, like not knowing you had a headache till it stops. And perhaps, as might happen, the giving of help and courage — even unknowingly — to a gay workmate tortured by the fear of 'being found out'. And last but far from least, the greatest pleasure of all — and sometimes the most hard-won — freedom.

from Man Alive *(Promo Issue, 1987)*

Personally Speaking

Sandra Marshall

Conscious of being lesbian at the age of eleven, I spent the next seventeen years repressing my true self, taking much spontaneity from my character. At twenty-eight, I began to find myself, having overcome the many spiritual depths I'd sunk to in my emotional isolation.

Reading in a Sunday paper (*Sunday Mail*, 7th September 1975) about a borstal boy being visited by the Glasgow Gay Advisory Service (CGAS) made tangible the knowledge that I did not have to seek out lurid London clubs to find other women like myself. I visited the official information bureau in George Square armed with paper and the names of two groups I wanted to get the telephone numbers of. My first group, Gingerbread, presented no problem. But the other — CGAS — well! I was given a card to copy from. This was held by the female clerk as one would hold out a photographic negative, saying, 'That number will put you in touch with the one you require.' I was given the address and telephone number of Iona Community House.

Can you imagine how I felt? I was tight with excitement. I called, got through and spoke to a man who sounded as ordinary and as sane as I thought I was. Eventually I went along to meetings at Community House; then the gay discos. After a spell of social self-indulgence, I remembered CGAS and how it had helped me. I volunteered and was accepted as a trainee and continue to be involved. I offer support — if able to — or just listen, as so many need to talk. Even now, as in the beginning, women are thin on the ground in the service. Glasgow, like other cities, needs its own Lesbian Switchboard. Many women, especially if they have a lesbian or feminist identity, do not want to be part of the male power structure that the male-dominated homophile groups have: those women with a commitment to women tend to form their own groups. This is really the best way for friendly co-existence. We should keep thinking about this . . . the politics of the situation can hardly be ignored as the personal is the political, especially for women in Scotland.

I find my own feelings in almost constant mental turmoil; of compromise in order to live barely above the poverty line, or, in socialising when men are around, I feel they are a potential threat. I believe our society breeds in the male potential murderers and rapists. My last comment needn't be as despairing as at first thought. You see, I have come to experience a great truth of life: love. Man is not the centre of all things. He may build and destroy in this life, mostly for his own ends, but through Jesus, and the enlightenment he gives, comes a greater life, a fulfilling love.

This is a testament of my faith — a very personal testament. I'm not really used to being so personal or so open about things in public but want to tell you of my great sadness in life. Over two years ago I became very close in friendship with another lesbian. We held each other in the greatest respect, we were sensitive to each other's vibrations. Our lives in their various aspects entwined to form a selfless love.

From our union we gave of ourselves in what way we could to those who sought or needed our support. Life was beautiful, fulfilled — the future needed no planning. Tomorrow would be as today . . . then came death.

I was talking to her at a women's group meeting — we were playing records. She died in my arms, before touching the floor. It was total loss: my life was void. Grief hit me in its fullest force much later. Initially, I had much support but then I became introverted. I wanted to be alone with my memories, our memories.

In our time together as lovers we had talked of life after death. We both believed strongly that that must be so. I'd read of automatic writing so in my grief I tried it, spending many hours holding a felt-tip pen over paper. When it worked, I was terrified. Then as it wrote out her name as a signature, I was filled with joy and wept. For ten days I spent all my spare time in a question-and-answer session till the experience started to confuse and hurt me, also — much to my horror — defile me.

I needed help and in desperation told a close friend who, with her lover, appeared an hour later to spend the night with me. They were both attacked, one having a violent headache, the other being possessed as I now realised I had been. This friend's possession was temporary as the entity left me to enter her. How thankful I was for the strength these two shared with me!

The following afternoon they returned with a spiritualist medium who told me because of my grieving and the fact that I was in an emotional void, the earthbound entity had attempted to take me over. No more writing but months of fear of darkness and inability to sleep by myself followed. My daughter, who was six years old at the time, was delighted to be sleeping in Mummy's bed and I was delighted to have her with me.

It's difficult to describe the mental agony of this situation, resulting also in rapid weight loss — not to mention the physical defilement. This took the form of masturbation, a mild sort of masturbation.

I came to realise that not even one's mind is one's private reserve but our thoughts are picked up and cannot only be read but given to us. What power, then, must prayer have if it be well intentioned?

I recalled that in the New Testament, in the life of Jesus as written in the first four books, there were many psychic happenings. I slowly read these four books and found much consolation, John 14 being, for me, profound. What followed was a delight — an inner peace. I have re-read this chapter many times — each time I am filled with thoughts of God's love.

I also read books of a spiritual content — not the statements of hauntings of the Edgar Allen Poe variety! A good example is *Testimony of Light* by Helen Grieves, who was in tune mentally with my friend, the late Frances Banks. This book was also a revelation, but work goes on, as does enlightenment, in God's kingdom, work I'm sure that must take many forms. Someone was, and probably is, with me, helping me in the little I am trying to do.

Last April, nearly a year ago, I had a most moving spiritual experience. My mind would not rest. The Gay Centre in Glasgow was deteriorating socially, so much so that it was coming to the state where women and others were feeling oppressed by the atmosphere created by insensitive youths who seemed to believe the Centre, including the back room (our only meeting-place), was their seven-nights-a-week preserve. Many responsible people had eventually given up and resigned from the Branch Committee. Some less established had just never returned because of the appalling behaviour.

What could I do? Putting my point across verbally at meetings without notes has never been my *forte,* which is why I decided to write to the editor of *Gay Scotland* in the hope that the situation would change for the better.

I was eager to have it done and drafted a copy at home that evening. It was a cold night. I changed, ready for bed, but I was warm for the room was warm, and so turned my gas fire down several times. Off came my dressing-gown. I finished the letter and was more than pleased with it. I had the strong feeling of help having been given so I clasped my hands and said a prayer, half mentally, half vocally, of thanks to God. I experienced my hands being numb and slightly swollen, then being pressed or clasped by an unseen force. This happened maybe four times. I opened my eyes — everything was as it should be, although my next-door neighbour was having a party and the noise of music and chatter was plainly audible. I remember feeling loved and at peace. An inner joy filled me. Pain entered my left arm and was for a short time, half a minute or so, quite hurtful. This was similar to, but much more intense than, the initial possession I had experienced.

I felt fear at this moment but it passed and I was calmed in thought when the sensation passed. I went to bed soon after. As I looked out of the window I noticed that frost was forming on cars. I got into bed beside my sleeping daughter, peeled aside all but one of the covers and went to sleep. I awoke after five in the morning. The heat was going but not completely gone. I replaced my blankets and went back to sleep.

extracted from a contribution to the Pastoral Approaches to Homosexuality *conference at Pitlochry in 1980*

Notes on Contributors

BRYAN ALLAN was born in Dunfermline, Fife. He lived abroad for several years before returning to Helensburgh, Dunbartonshire. He now lives in London where he is involved with *Square Peg* magazine. He is currently working on a collection of short stories and also writes poetry when the Muse permits. Favourite colour is blue.

TOMMY BARCLAY is Gorbals born and now lives and works near Manchester. He has been published in *Gay News, Mancunian Gay, Gay Life* and various anthologies by Northern Gay Writers, of which he is a member. Likes books, music, peace. Dislikes sleazy tabloids, hypocritical censors, Victorian values. Beginning masterpiece first thing tomorrow.

JANE CARNALL writes: 'I was born in Edinburgh in 1967 and have lived there all my life; I've always been fascinated by science-fiction and began writing sf about six years ago. I'm a sharemother to at least four cats, I like computers, and I keep a labyris in the closet. I also write non-fiction, most of which has been published by *Gay Scotland*.'

TONI DAVIDSON is hanging on obsessively to twenty-three and lives in Glasgow. Spends most of his time teasing with horror and comforting with heroes. Between aesthetic dead-ends and nights staring at a typewriter, he ekes a living out of selling his arse and getting into debt. At the moment he is just finishing a collection of nasty, violent, sex-obsessed, so-called short stories.

Hi, I'm HELEN. No doubt some of you are too. Hope you like the poem. I have a cat and a guinea-pig called Winston-Basil. My two sons are pretty silly too.

RAB HENDERSON was born in fornication 1870, Blebo. Orraman on muckle fairmtouns roon east Fife. Mony fremmit adventures, accoonts o which wur fun amang his papers efter his deith in 1950, an wur prentit in *Gay Scotland* in the early 1980s. Immortalised in the sey *'as haird as Henderson's erse'*.

HUBERT KENNEDY is a former historian of mathematics and the author of *Ulrichs: The Life and Works of Karl Heinrich Ulrichs, Pioneer of the Modern Gay Movement* (1988). He is the editor-translator of John Henry Mackay's *The Hustler* (1985) and *Fenny Skaller and other Prose Writings from the Books of the Nameless Love* (1988).

GEORGE MCALPINE is twenty-six and lives just outside Glasgow. In the past he's been a student, worked as a waiter, a barman, in an office and is now a nurse. He writes mostly about sex — a habit he's trying to get out of.

IONA MCGREGOR writes: 'I spent my early childhood trailing after the defenders of the (now extinct) British Empire. Education see-sawed between Scotland, England and Wales, and I became a reluctant teacher for most of my employable life. Now a full-time writer and happy GOPPIE (Gay Older Person), I live in Edinburgh.'

JOHN MCRAE was born in Perth and lives in Italy. He divides his time between theatre (director at Abeliano Theatre, Bari), publishing and university (the new university of Basilicata). He edited *Teleny* and Forrest Reid's *Tom Barber* trilogy for GMP and published poems in the anthology *Not Love Alone* and in *So Long Desired* with James Kirkup.

EDWIN MORGAN writes: 'Born in Glasgow 1920. At present Visiting Professor in English Studies at the University of Strathclyde. Books of poetry include *Poems of Thirty Years, Sonnets from Scotland, Selected Poems, From the Video Box,* and *Themes on a Variation*. Published a volume of translations of the gay German poet August Graf von Platen in 1978.'

SIGRID NIELSEN came to Scotland in 1979 and is co-founder of Lavender Menace Bookshop (now West and Wilde) in

Edinburgh. This short story is a collision between two novels, *The Sorceress Graeylaw*, about Catriona and Anne, and *Liberties,* a novel about Jean, Céline and three other gay characters in the French Revolution.

WALTER PERRIE lives in internal exile in Perthshire. He has produced five collections of poetry, for some of which he has been villainously abused. He has also produced a body of critical writings but in early middle age has taken to hill-climbing and drink as antidotes to the Scottish literary scene. He now co-edits *Margin*, an international arts quarterly.

ALEX RAINBOW writes: 'I'm very glad that "Mine Own Nature" is being included in an anthology now because I originally wrote it for a women-only anthology under the auspices of Sheba Press, they rejected it because they considered it "too odd" and "too intense". I'm now on an enterprise allowance as a freelance writer with particular interest in women and science.'

PETER D. ROBINSON is an almost mature student at Stirling University. Writing has always been a hobby (as has paper shredding). Being one half of a long-standing pretend family relationship, Peter gathered enough material before meeting Iain to keep him writing well into the next century. Printable interests include reading, music and theatre.

SIMON TAYLOR was born in Dunfermline in 1950 and was educated there and at St Andrews. He taught English in Germany for two years. Engaged and disengaged, St Andrews again to do post-grad degree in Anglo-Saxon and to come out. After doing residential social work in Reading, he moved to Edinburgh in 1978 where he still lives. He was addicted to meetings (SCRAM, Gay Switchboard, Gay Scotland, SAM), and is now allergic to them. He works as a freelance tourist guide (German, French) in summer, writing gay historical novels in winter, and lives with the sculptor L. A. Reid and several dogs.

FRED URQUHART was born in 1912 and is one of Scotland's best known short story writers. He has published twelve collections of stories and novellas. His stories have been broadcast, translated and printed in many anthologies. *Full Time*, a selection of stories, has just been published by Aberdeen University Press. He has also published four novels. His first novel, *Time Will Knit*, has just celebrated its fiftieth anniversary by being republished in paperback by Richard Drew's Scottish Collections. Urquhart's new novel has a homosexual theme. He loathes the word 'gay' and insists it should be used only in its old sense to denote joyfulness.

CHRISTOPHER WHYTE was born in Glasgow in 1952 and was educated at St Aloysius College then Cambridge and after that Perugia. He returned in 1985 after eleven years in Italy and now teaches Scottish Literature in Edinburgh. He is putting together a collection of poems in Gaelic and working in a desultory way at a novel and a book of short stories in English.

IAN WYLIE writes: 'The back cover artist was born one of a set of twins in Govan 1962. He is intensely shy and would prefer to let his cover do the talking.'